Plastering

CONSTRUCTION SERIES

Plastering

CONSTRUCTION SERIES

www.skills2learn.com
Experts in e-learning & virtual reality simulation

CENGAGE
Learning™

Australia • Brazil • Japan • Korea • Mexico • Singapore • Spain • United Kingdom • United States

Plastering
Skills2Learn

Publishing Director: Linden Harris

Commissioning Editor: Lucy Mills

Development Editor: Helen Green

Editorial Assistant: Claire Napoli

Project Editor: Lucy Arthy

Production Controller: Eyvett Davis

Marketing Manager: Jason Bennett

Typesetter: MPS Limited, a Macmillan Company

Cover design: HCT Creative

Text design: Design Deluxe

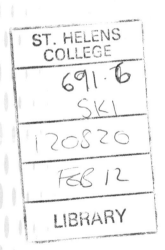

For product information and technology assistance,
contact **emea.info@cengage.com**.

For permission to use material from this text or product,
and for permission queries,
email **emea.permissions@cengage.com**.

DISCLAIMER

This publication has been developed by Cengage Learning. It is intended as a method of studying and to assist in training in relation to its subject matter and should be used only as part of a comprehensive training programme with tutor guidance. Cengage Learning has taken all reasonable care in the preparation of this publication but Cengage Learning and Skills2Learn and its partners accept no liability howsoever in respect of any breach of the rights of any third party howsoever occasioned or damage caused to any third party as a result of this publication. The information contained in the publication is not a substitute for manufacturer's guidelines or current legislation. Cengage Learning and Skills2Learn and its partners do not endorse or recommend any of the proprietary products that may be named in the publication.

British Library Cataloguing-in-Publication Data

A catalogue record for this book is available from the British Library.

ISBN: 978-1-4080-4186-4

Cengage Learning EMEA

Cheriton House, North Way, Andover, Hampshire, SP10 5BE
United Kingdom

Cengage Learning products are represented in Canada by Nelson Education Ltd.

For your lifelong learning solutions, visit **www.cengage.co.uk**

Purchase your next print book, e-book or e-chapter at **www.cengagebrain.com**

Printed in Malta by Melita Press
1 2 3 4 5 6 7 8 9 10 – 14 13 12

Contents

Foreword

The construction industry is a significant part of the UK economy and a major employer of people. It has a huge impact on the environment and plays a role in our everyday life in many ways. With environmental issues such as climate change and sustainable sourcing of materials now playing an important part in the design and construction of buildings and other structures, there is a need to educate and re-educate those new to the industry and those currently involved.

This construction series of e-learning programmes and text workbooks has been developed to provide a structured blended learning approach that will enhance the learning experience and stimulate a deeper understanding of the construction trades and give an awareness of sustainability issues. The content within these learning materials has been aligned to units of the Plastering, National Occupational Standards, and can be used as a support tool whilst studying for relevant vocational qualifications.

The uniqueness of this construction series is that it aims to bridge the gap between classroom-based and practical-based learning. The workbooks provide classroom-based activities that can involve learners in discussions and research tasks as well as providing them with understanding and knowledge of the subject. The e-learning programmes take the subject further, with high quality images, animations and audio further enhancing the content and showing information in a different light. In addition, the e-practical side of the e-learning places the learner in a virtual environment where they can move around freely, interact with objects and use the knowledge and skills they have gained from the workbook and e-learning to complete a set of tasks whilst in the comfort of a safe working environment.

The workbooks and e-learning programmes are designed to help learners continuously improve their skills and provide confidence and a sound knowledge base before getting their hands dirty in the real world.

About the Construction Consortia

This series of construction workbooks and e-learning programmes have been developed by the E-Construction Consortium. The consortium is a group of colleges and organizations that are passionate about the construction industry and are determined to enhance the learning experiences of people within the different trades or those that are new to it.

The consortium members have many years' experience in the construction and educational sectors and have created this blended learning approach of interactive e-learning programmes and text workbooks to achieve the aim of:

- Providing accessible training in different areas of construction.
- Bridging the gap between classroom-based and practical-based learning.
- Providing a concentrated set of improvement learning modules.
- Enabling learners to gain new skills and qualifications more effectively.
- Improving functional skills and awareness of sustainability issues within the industry.
- Promoting health and safety in the industry.
- Encouraging training and continuous professional development.

For more information about this construction series please visit: **www.e-construction.co.uk** or **www.skills2learn.com**.

About e-learning

INTRODUCTION

This construction series of workbooks and e-learning programmes use a blended learning approach to train learners in construction skills. Blended learning allows training to be delivered through different mediums such as books, e-learning (computer-based training), practical workshops and traditional classroom techniques. These training methods are designed to complement each other and work in tandem to achieve overall learning objectives and outcomes.

E-LEARNING

The Plastering e-learning programme that is also available to sit alongside this workbook offers a different method of learning. With technology playing an increasingly important part of everyday life, e-learning uses visually rich 2D and 3D graphics/animation, audio, video, text and interactive quizzes, to allow you to engage with the content and learn at your own pace and in your own time.

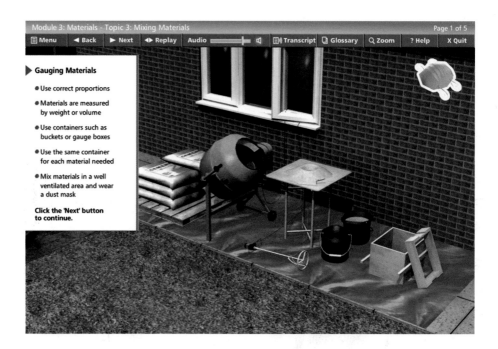

E-PRACTICAL

Part of the e-learning programme is an e-practical interactive scenario. This facility allows you to be immersed in a virtual reality situation where the choices you make affect the outcome. Using 3D technology, you can move freely around the environment, interact with objects, carry out tests, and make decisions and mistakes until you have mastered the subject. By practising in a virtual environment you will not only be able to see what you've learnt but also analyze your approach and thought process to the problem.

BENEFITS OF E-LEARNING

Diversity – E-Learning can be used for almost anything. With the correct approach any subject can be brought to life to provide an interactive training experience.

Technology – Advancements in computer technology now allow a wide range of spectacular and engaging e-learning to be delivered to a wider population.

Captivate and Motivate – Hold the learner's attention for longer with the use of high quality graphics, animation, sound and interactivity.

Safe Environment – E-Practical scenarios can create environments which simulate potentially harmful real-life situations or replicate a piece of dangerous equipment, therefore allowing the learner to train and gain experience and knowledge in a completely safe environment.

Instant Feedback – Learners can undertake training assessments that feed back results instantly. This can provide information on where they need to re-study or congratulate them on passing the assessment. Results and Certificates can also be printed for future records.

On-Demand – Can be accessed 24 hours a day, 7 days a week, 365 days of the year. You can access the content at any time and view it at your own pace.

Portable Solutions – Can be delivered via a CD, website or LMS. Learners no longer need to travel to all lectures, conferences, meetings or training days. This saves many man-hours in reduced travelling, cost of hotels and expenses amongst other things.

Reduction of Costs – Can be used to teach best practice processes on jobs which use large quantities or expensive materials. Learners can practise their techniques and boost their confidence to a high enough standard before being allowed near real materials.

PLASTERING E-LEARNING

The aim of the plastering e-learning programme is to enhance a learner's knowledge and understanding of the plastering trade. The course content is aligned to units from the Plastering; National Occupational Standards (NOS) so can be used for study towards certification.

The programme gives the learners an understanding of the technicalities of plastering as well as looking at sustainability, health and safety and functional skills in an interactive and visually engaging manner. It also provides a 'real-life' scenario where the learner can apply the knowledge gained from the tutorials in a safe yet practical way.

By using and completing this programme, it is expected that learners will:

- Understand the role of the plasterer in the working environment and have knowledge of some of the tools that will be used.
- Understand the different backgrounds that can be plastered/ rendered.
- Be able to explain the choice of materials for a project, calculate the correct quantities, source these from an appropriate supplier, and identify the correct disposal method for waste materials.
- Understand the preparation and procedures for rendering exterior surfaces.
- Understand the sequence of work and procedures for plastering interior surfaces.

The e-learning programme is divided into the following learning modules:

- Getting Started
- Backgrounds
- Materials
- External Rendering
- Internal Plastering
- End Test
- Interactive E-Practical Scenario

THE CONSTRUCTION SERIES

As part of the construction series the following e-learning programmes and workbooks are available. For more information please contact the sales team on **emea.fesales@cengage.com** or visit the website **www.e-construction.co.uk**.

- Plastering
- Bricklaying
- Carpentry & Joinery
- Painting & Decorating
- Wall & Floor Tiling

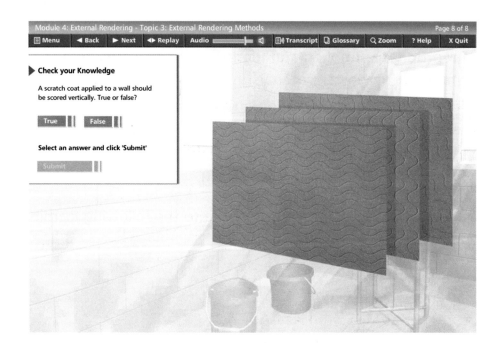

About the NOS

The National Occupational Standards (NOS) provide a framework of information that outline the skills, knowledge and understanding required to carry out work-based activities within a given vocation. Each standard is divided into units that cover specific activities of that occupation. Employers, employees, teachers and learners can use these standards as information, support and a reference resource that will enable them to understand the skills and criteria required for good practice in the workplace.

The standards are used as a basis to develop many vocational qualifications in the United Kingdom for a wide range of occupations. This workbook and associated e-learning programme are aligned to the Plastering, National Occupational Standards, and the information within relates to the following units:

- Conform to General Workplace Safety
- Conform to Efficient Work Practices
- Move and Handle Resources
- Prepare and Mix Plastering Materials
- Prepare Background Surfaces for Plasterwork
- Position and Secure Plasterwork Resources
- Produce Internal Solid Plastering Finishes
- Produce External Solid Render Finishes
- Install Direct Bond Dry Linings
- Lay Sand and Cement Screeds
- Position and Secure Fibrous Plaster Components
- Confirm Work Activities and Resources for Work
- Develop and Maintain Good Working Relationships
- Confirm the Occupational Method of Work

About the book

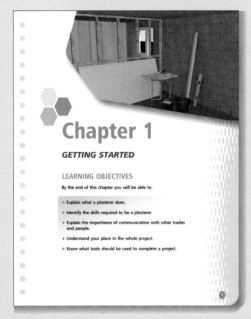

Learning Objectives at the start of each chapter explain the skills and knowledge you need to be proficient in and understand by the end of the chapter.

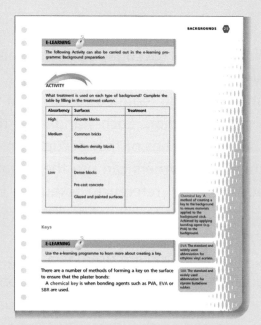

Activities are practical tasks that engage you in the subject and further your understanding.

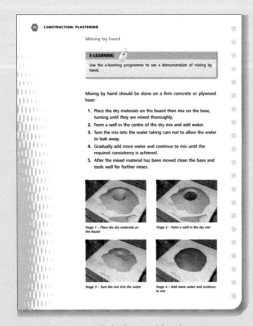

E-Learning Icons link the workbook content to the e-learning programme.

Sustainability Boxes provide information and helpful advice on how to work in a sustainable and environmentally friendly way.

Note on UK Standards draws your attention to relevant building regulations.

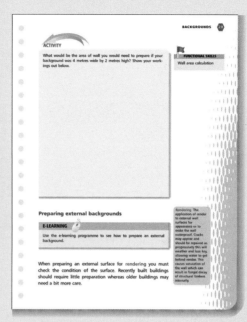

Functional Skills icons highlight activities that develop and test your Maths, English and ICT key skills.

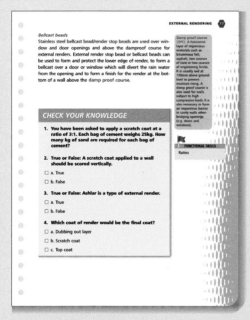

Check Your Knowledge at the end of each chapter to test your knowledge and understanding.

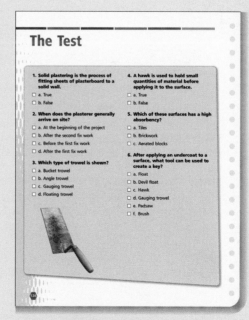

End test in Chapter 6 checks your knowledge on all the information within the workbook.

Chapter 1

GETTING STARTED

LEARNING OBJECTIVES

By the end of this chapter you will be able to:

- Explain what a plasterer does.

- Identify the skills required to be a plasterer.

- Explain the importance of communication with other trades and people.

- Understand your place in the whole project.

- Know what tools should be used to complete a project.

Plaster A colourless, white or pinkish mineral formed from heating gypsum at high temperatures. Plaster is used to protect and enhance the appearance of the surface as it provides a joint-less finish.

Cement A grey or white powdery material made from chalk or limestone and clay. Cement is the most common binder in bricklaying mortar and works by hardening as a result of a chemical reaction when mixed with water. The most common type of cement is Ordinary Portland Cement (OPC).

Sand Fine aggregate that is one of the raw ingredients for mixing mortar.

Plasterboard A type of board made of gypsum sandwiched between sheets of paper. It has a number of properties and can be made to different thicknesses and sizes for different areas and uses.

Cornice A decorative moulding at the junction between the walls and ceiling of a room.

NOS REFERENCE

Conform to efficient work practices

Confirm work activities and resources for work

Confirm the occupational method of work

Develop and maintain good working relationships

Prepare and mix plastering materials

INTRODUCTION

What is a plasterer?

Plasterers mix and apply **plaster** and other materials such as **cement** and **sand** to the internal and external surfaces of buildings. The material protects, insulates and enhances the appearance of the surface providing a suitable finish.

Plasterers can work on major projects such as large commercial developments, new build housing or on small scale work such as extensions, repairs and restoration jobs.

There are three areas of plastering work:

● Solid plastering where a protective finish is applied to interior or exterior surfaces.

● Dry lining which involves fitting sheets of **plasterboard** to a framework or directly to a background using a specialist adhesive.

● Fibrous plastering or making ornamental plasterwork such as **cornices**.

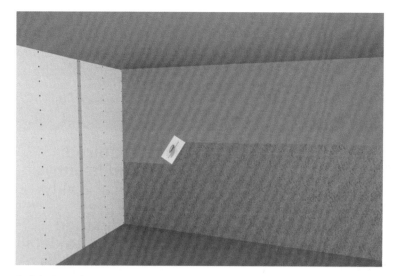

Solid plastering

Dry lining

Fibrous plastering

Skills required by a plasterer

JOB VACANCY

Job Title:
Plasterer

Location:
Nationwide

Hours:
Average 37.5 hours per week

Work Pattern:
Monday to Friday

Skills Required:
- Fit and healthy
- Practical ability
- Hand-eye co-ordination
- Attention to detail
- Numeracy skills
- Part of a team
- Artistic ability
- Working safely

NOTE ON UK STANDARDS

It is possible to train as a plasterer at any age. Most people train on the job as well as attending a college or training centre to gain qualifications or train through a construction apprenticeship.

COMMUNICATION

This section looks at the importance of the building design documents, the job of the plasterer on site and working together with other people.

Building design

Each building job will have a design specification document and a bill of quantities. These documents will contain:

- Detailed plans of the build.
- Information on how the construction should be built.
- A list of materials that need to be used and their quantities.

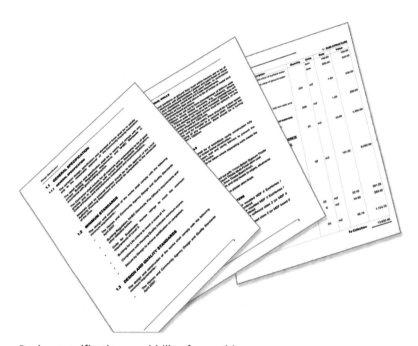

Design specifications and bills of quantities

NOTE ON UK STANDARDS

These documents will be required to satisfy and comply with building regulations and meet the approval of local authorities. You will need to refer to and understand these documents to make sure the building is constructed correctly.

Joist A beam that supports a ceiling or floor.

Stud The timber posts within a timber-frame wall.

The plasterer on site

Plasterers arrive on site after the first fix work, this is when the **joists**, floors and **stud** walls are erected and the wiring for the electrical supply and pipes for the water supply are fitted.

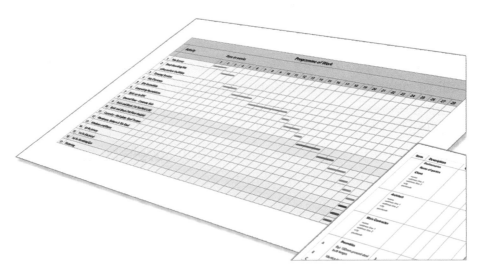

Example of work documents

The plasterer's job is to finish internal and external walls, floors and ceilings by applying different materials to produce a **plumb**, **level** and flat finish. This can include preparing surfaces, preparing the plaster or **render** mix and applying the mix on the surface. Depending upon the type of surface, this may require a number of coats and each coat may need to set and be keyed before the next is applied.

Plumb The vertical level of a surface or structure.

Level The horizontal level of a surface or structure.

Render A sand and cement backing coat for tiling, usually applied in at least two coats.

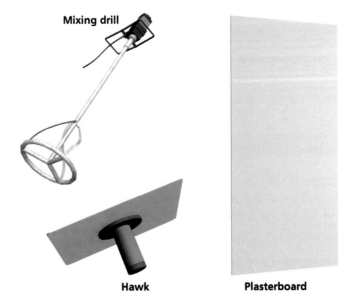

Mixing drill

Hawk   Plasterboard

Plasterers will need to be able to fit different types of plasterboard depending on the specification document. They will also need to finish the surface off to a high standard for the next stage of the construction process.

Working together

The plasterer might not always work directly with other trades such as the bricklayer or the electrician, however, good communication is important. The consequences of poor communication can include late completion of work or work having to be redone.

It is also important that each trade leaves the work to an acceptable standard for the next trade. Bricklayers must make sure that the walls are plumb and clean for the plasterer to work on. As the plasterer you must make sure that the surfaces are level and clean for the painter and decorator and socket boxes are free of plaster for the electrician.

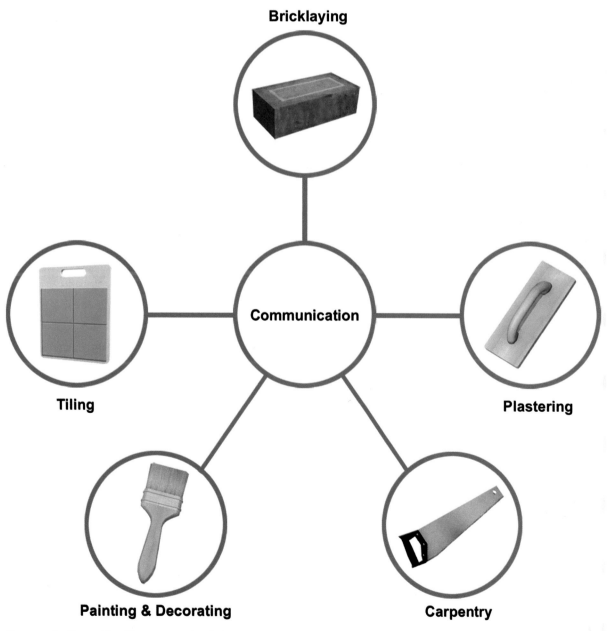

Communication with other groups is vital

TOOLS

In this section we shall look at some of the tools you will use as a plasterer. Some of these are specific to the plastering trade whilst others are commonly used across the construction industry.

HEALTH & SAFETY

All the tools you will use are potentially dangerous. Observe all relevant health and safety instructions and wear the correct **personal protective equipment** for the tool you are using.

Make sure you use the right tool for the job. Do not use damaged or defective tools, do not play with tools, especially power tools, and do not use a tool that you are not properly trained to use.

Personal Protective Equipment (PPE)
Depending on the type of work, there are different types of equipment specifically designed to protect your health and safety. Examples include gloves, safety boots, goggles and dust mask.

Ensure your tools are clean before and after use otherwise the setting time of future plaster mixes will be affected.

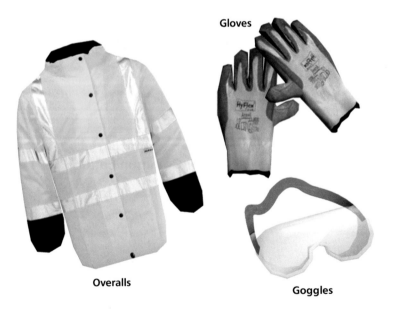

Gloves

Overalls

Goggles

The plasterer's tools

The plasterer uses a number of different hand tools such as:

- trowels
- hawk and spot board
- floats
- rules and edges
- brushes
- buckets.

Trowels

The plasterer uses a variety of **trowels**:

- The **gauging trowel** is used to mix small measures of material. It can also be used for placing plaster in awkward areas.
- The **bucket trowel** has a square edge and is used for scraping plaster from the bottom of the bucket.
- The **plasterer's trowel**, when new, is used for heavier work such as undercoats. When it becomes worn in with slightly rounded corners it is used as a finishing trowel to provide a smooth finish.

Trowel A range of hand held tools used to mix, apply and spread or remove materials. There are many different types of trowels for different purposes including bucket trowel, gauge trowel, notched trowel and pointing trowel.

Gauging trowel A popular trowel used for the mixing, bedding and placing of materials.

Bucket trowel A trowel with a square metal edge used for scraping material from the bottom of the bucket.

Plasterer's trowel When new a plasterer's trowel is used for applying plaster undercoats, but when used and worn with slightly rounded edges it is used for finishing plaster coats.

Plasterer's trowel   **Gauging trowel**   **Bucket trowel**

Hawk A square metal piece with a handle for holding small quantities of materials, e.g. plaster, within easy reach when applying to a wall.

Spot board A piece of ply placed on a stand that is used as a holding area for larger amounts of material, e.g. plaster. The plasterer will generally transfer the materials from the spot board to the hawk ready for applying to the surface.

Plasterer's float A float used for render work.

Devil float A float with nails protruding from the bottom used to scratch backgrounds for plastering or rendering to ensure materials stick to the background.

Key The preparation to backgrounds either chemically, mechanically, hacking or scratching before plaster or render is applied. Creating keys ensure that the plaster or render sticks and the method of keying will depend on the type of background.

Float A range of tools which can be made from a variety of materials with a grip that holds a thin flat base approximately 100mm × 250mm. There are a number of different floats for different purposes including plasterer's float, devil float and grout float.

Modern trowels are usually made of stainless steel with soft handles and come in a range of sizes depending on the work being carried out. It is important to always keep your trowel clean.

Hawk and spot board

The **hawk** or hand board is a square piece of metal, wood or plastic with a handle on the base. It is used to hold small quantities of material within easy reach when applying it to the surface. When choosing a hawk, make sure it is fairly light and comfortable as you will be holding it for long periods.

The **spot board** is a piece of plywood placed on a stand that is used as a holding area for larger amounts of material. The plasterer will generally transfer the materials from the spot board to the hawk ready for applying to the surface.

Plasterer's hawk   Spot board

Floats

The **plasterer's float** is mainly used for flooring and rendering.

The **devil float** has nails protruding from its base and is used to **key** the surface to make sure the plaster sticks and for filling in small hollows. **Floats** are usually made of wood or plastic and should be washed immediately after use.

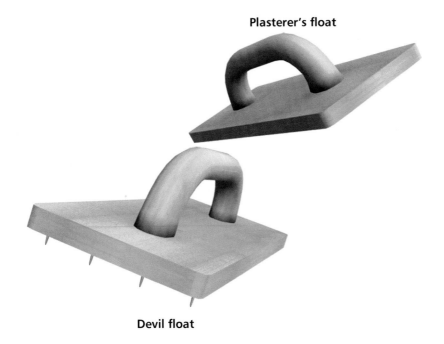

Plasterer's float

Devil float

Rules and edges

The plasterer uses a number of rules such as the Darby rule and the feather edge rule to level off surfaces. The rule is also used to check that the line of a wall is true. There are two main types of feather edges: trapezoidal and h-section.

Darby rule A straight-edged rule used to level off surfaces.

Feather edge A straight-edged rule used to level off surfaces.

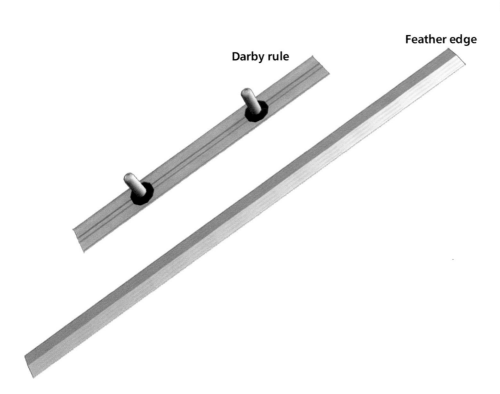

Darby rule

Feather edge

ACTIVITY

What do you think a trapezoidal feather edge and an h-section feather edge look like? Draw a picture of each in the boxes provided.

Brushes

The plasterer will use a brush for a number of different purposes during the plastering process including splashing the wall with water to test for absorbency. You can use a broom to dust down and clean surfaces.

Broom

Brush

Buckets

Buckets are used for gauging or measuring quantities of materials, mixing materials and carrying materials and tools. They should be cleaned out immediately after use.

Buckets ready for use

ACTIVITY

The wordsearch below contains a number of other tools and equipment that a plasterer will use. Can you find them all?

```
J  R  H  E  B  O  C  O  T  G  E  O  E  D  T
O  E  T  N  O  H  E  I  R  A  W  F  R  L  A
I  M  A  I  B  A  C  B  S  A  I  Y  L  C  P
N  M  B  L  B  M  T  I  S  N  W  I  L  E  E
T  A  G  K  M  N  O  D  K  A  R  S  R  M  M
C  H  N  L  U  T  A  Y  L  D  R  P  I  E  E
O  H  I  A  L  P  E  L  C  E  T  I  S  N  A
M  C  X  H  P  L  S  I  M  O  T  N  O  T  S
P  T  I  C  N  C  R  M  N  L  S  S  F  M  U
O  U  M  A  R  T  A  T  E  O  A  N  I  I  R
U  C  T  E  C  H  B  E  T  N  W  I  I  X  E
N  S  W  E  H  G  F  T  M  O  R  T  R  E  B
D  S  L  T  S  C  R  I  M  T  A  P  E  R  C
C  E  A  R  E  X  I  M  R  E  W  O  P  O  L
O  L  H  I  O  O  H  A  E  E  E  O  S  I  T
```

JOINT COMPOUND, DRYWALL SCREWS, ELECTRIC DRILL, SCUTCH HAMMER, STANLEY KNIFE, TAPE MEASURE, CEMENT MIXER, LATH HAMMER, POWER MIXER, MIXING BATH, CHALK LINE, SCRIM TAPE, TIN SNIPS, PLUMB BOB, PAD SAW, SAW

CHECK YOUR KNOWLEDGE

1. **Match up the images of the tools shown here with their correct names and descriptions.**

Task	Tool	Name
Measuring and mixing quantities of material		Bucket
Mixing small amounts of plaster and placing in awkward areas		Gauging trowel
Holding plaster prior to applying to surface		Brush
Wetting the surface		Hawk
Keying the surface		Devil float

2. **Name the three types of trowel used by a plasterer that have been described in this chapter.**

3. **True or False: Fibrous plastering is when a finish is applied to interior or exterior surfaces.**

☐ a. True

☐ b. False

4. **True or False: Plasterers arrive on site during the first fix stage of work.**

☐ a. True

☐ b. False

5. **Which trowel is used to mix small measures of plastering material?**

☐ a. The gauging trowel

☐ b. The bucket trowel

☐ c. The plasterer's trowel

Chapter 2

BACKGROUNDS

LEARNING OBJECTIVES

By the end of this chapter you will be able to:

- List the steps required to prepare the working area.

- Explain the factors that need to be taken into consideration when preparing backgrounds.

- List the specific requirements for interior and exterior backgrounds.

NOS REFERENCE

Conform to general workplace safety

Prepare background surfaces for plasterwork

INTRODUCTION

Preparing the work area

Background General term used for the surface to which materials are adhered.

Before preparing the **background** surface you will need to prepare the working area to ensure that the area is safe and to protect the property and its contents from damage.

Internal areas

When working inside make sure that you have adequate lighting and your materials are close at hand. In all situations remove any moveable items and cover the floor area. If some items or special features can't be moved then make sure they are fully covered as well.

HEALTH & SAFETY

You should seek advice from a qualified electrician when working near any electrical supplies or fittings.

External areas

If you are working externally you will need to ensure the working area is clear. Be aware of areas that could be damaged whilst you are working. You may need to protect surrounding surfaces.

HEALTH & SAFETY

Remove any items that might present a hazard when working and tape the area to ensure other trades or members of the public do not wander into your place of work.

Preparing the external area

BACKGROUND PREPARATION

Types of background

Before you begin plastering you will need to prepare the background. The preparation is crucial to ensuring the work is completed to the highest standard. The type of preparation will depend upon the type of background you will be plastering. Typical backgrounds could include:

- various types and ages of brick and blockwork (**engineering brick**, aircrete **block**)

- plasterboard

- expanded metal lath

- painted surfaces.

Engineering brick A strong and dense type of brick, impervious to water so ideal for use in damp areas.

Block The most common block type is aggregate concrete blocks. They have a large number of desirable properties including high sound and thermal insulation and excellent moisture, fire and frost resistance. They are strong, lightweight, easy to work with and easy to fix to. Blocks are manufactured in solid, hollow and cellular block forms and one type of block can be used in every situation on a site.

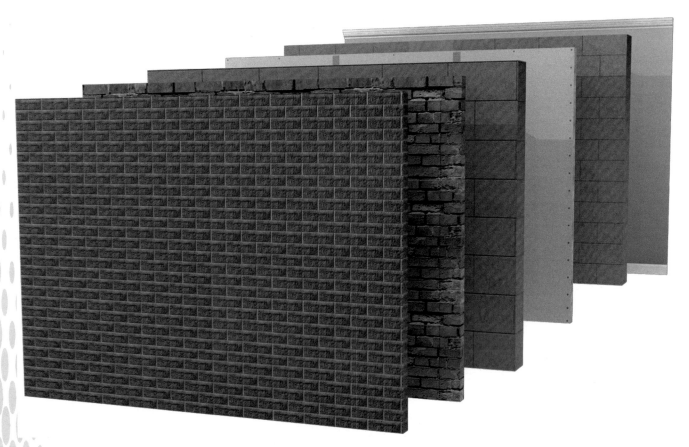

Different types of background

Preparing the background

For all types of background some basic preparation work is required. This can include:

- Brushing down the surface to remove any loose materials.
- Removing any bits of sand or cement left over from laying the bricks.
- Making a key for the background.
- Testing the background for suction.
- Treating with a bonding agent if necessary.
- Fixing expanded metal lath or EML to surfaces made up of different materials.
- Fixing angle beads at external angles.
- Setting up the spot board and stand to hold the material as you use it.

EML The standard and widely used abbreviation for Expanded Metal Lathing.

Angle bead Steel strips fixed at external corners to provide a continuous guide when plastering.

Brushing down the surface

Testing for suction

Fixing angle beads

Background considerations

There are a number of factors that need to be taken into account when considering the preparation of a background. These include:

- The type and condition of the current background.
- Whether it requires a chemical or **mechanical key** to make the plaster bond.
- The amount of suction or absorbency of the background and whether the background is likely to shrink or move.

Suction

Mechanical key The recess in mortar joints by 10mm between brickwork or blockwork before plastering or rendering to ensure the plaster or render sticks.

E-LEARNING

Use the e-learning programme to learn more about how suction affects plastering.

For plaster to set it needs to retain as much water as possible. The water causes a chemical reaction called hydration to occur and the longer the water stays in the plaster the better the setting process will be.

Suction is the ability of a background to absorb water. If it sucks in too much water (high suction) the plaster may shrink or crack as the water is pulled from it too quickly. If the water is not sucked in (low suction) then the plaster may not bond.

You can test for the absorbency rate of the background you are working on by splashing water on it. The length of time it takes for the water to soak in will give you an idea of the absorbency rate. Suction can be treated with a bonding agent such as **PVA**.

PVA The standard and widely used abbreviation for Polyvinyl Acetate.

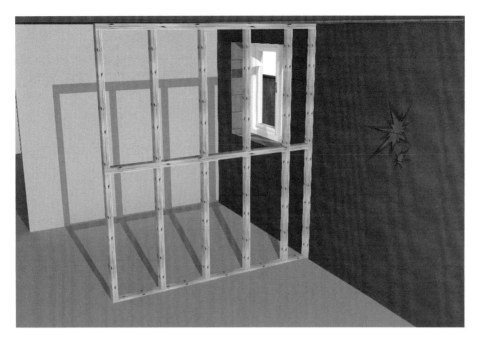

High suction problems e.g. cracking

Low suction problems e.g. slippage

ACTIVITY

Can you suggest three factors that may influence the suction and absorbency rates of a background?

High absorbent surfaces

High absorbent surfaces should be pre-treated with water or a propriety agent; this will stop the plaster drying out too quickly. Types of high absorbent surfaces include:

- aircrete blocks.

Medium absorbent surfaces

Medium absorbent surfaces should be cleaned of all dust and debris. Types of medium absorbent surfaces are:

- common bricks
- medium density blocks
- plasterboard.

Low absorbent surfaces

Glaze A ceramic coating in a glassy state or the material from which this coating is made.

Low absorbent surfaces should have a thistle bonding coat applied to them. Glazed and painted surfaces should also be pre-treated with a bonding agent. Types of low absorbent surfaces are:

- dense blocks
- pre-cast concrete
- glazed and painted surfaces.

E-LEARNING

The following Activity can also be carried out in the e-learning programme: Background preparation

ACTIVITY

What treatment is used on each type of background? Complete the table by filling in the treatment column.

Absorbency	Surfaces	Treatment
High	Aircrete blocks	
Medium	Common bricks	
	Medium density blocks	
	Plasterboard	
Low	Dense blocks	
	Pre-cast concrete	
	Glazed and painted surfaces	

Keys

E-LEARNING

Use the e-learning programme to learn more about creating a key.

There are a number of methods of forming a key on the surface to ensure that the plaster bonds:

A **chemical key** is when bonding agents such as PVA, **EVA** or **SBR** are used.

Chemical key A method of creating a key to the background to ensure materials applied to the background stick. Achieved by applying bonding agent (e.g. PVA) to the background.

EVA The standard and widely used abbreviation for ethylene vinyl acetate.

SBR The standard and widely used abbreviation for styrene butadiene rubber.

Chemical key

Hacking A method of creating a key to the background to ensure materials applied to the background stick. Achieved by physically hacking a background with a scutch hammer.

Scutch hammer A doubled-ended hammer made with long thin steel blades about 30mm wide acting as chisels. The scutch hammer is used for hacking the surfaces of brickwork to create a key for rendering.

Brickwork A solid wall built of bricks, laid to bond and in mortar. Used to be the most common load-bearing external wall construction. Mainly finished with fair faced bricks and pointed or rendered. Minimal maintenance required but as properties age partial or complete re-pointing or re-rendering respectively may become necessary.

A mechanical key is created by using a range of tools to make a smooth surface rough. This rough texture helps the plaster adhere to the surface. An example of how to create a mechanical key is **hacking**. This can be done with a tool such as a **scutch hammer** on block or **brickwork** or a devil float on sand and cement mixes or lightweight plaster.

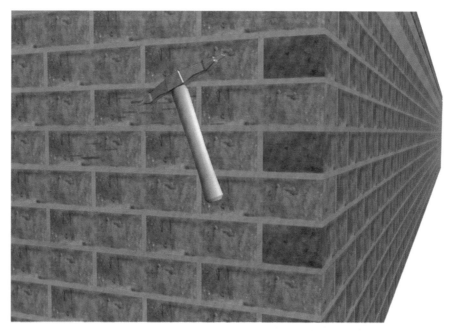

Mechanical key

ACTIVITY

What PPE do you need when creating a mechanical key? List six items below.

Shrinkage and movement

Weather conditions and the temperature may cause the background to shrink and expand but movement beads can be fixed to the wall to allow for up to 6mm of movement.

Structural movement may also occur because of the design of the background, for example where two different materials meet such as blockwork and concrete. This can be resolved by fixing EML to the area.

Movement beads fixed to surfaces

INTERIOR AND EXTERIOR BACKGROUNDS

Preparing internal backgrounds

E-LEARNING

Use the e-learning programme to see how to prepare an internal background.

Your method of preparation will depend on the surface but you will generally brush down and remove any dirt or materials, then test for absorbency by splashing water on the surface and observing how it soaks in.

High suction backgrounds would be prepared by wetting them down or sealing with a proprietary bonding agent. Low suctions would have a scratch coat applied to them.

> **Scratch coat** The first coat applied to the wall when three coat work is required, keyed with a devil float.

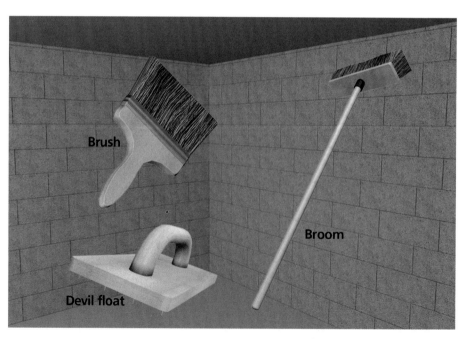

Preparing internal backgrounds with different tools

ACTIVITY

What would be the area of wall you would need to prepare if your background was 4 metres wide by 2 metres high? Show your workings out below.

FUNCTIONAL SKILLS

Wall area calculation

Preparing external backgrounds

E-LEARNING

Use the e-learning programme to see how to prepare an external background.

When preparing an external surface for rendering you must check the condition of the surface. Recently built buildings should require little preparation whereas older buildings may need a bit more care.

Rendering The application of render to external wall surfaces for appearance or to make the wall waterproof. Cracks may appear and should be repaired as progressively this will weather and lose key, allowing water to get behind render. This causes saturation of the wall which can result in fungal decay of structural timbers internally.

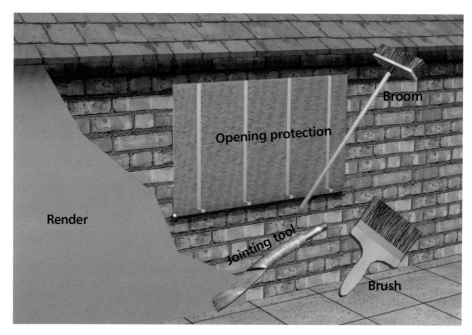

Preparing exterior backgrounds with different tools

Always brush down to get rid of any loose materials. Older buildings may require any old render to be removed and any loose **mortar** joints to be raked out. You need to make sure all window and door openings are protected.

Mortar A mixture of sand, cement (sometimes with lime and/or additives) and water, used to bond stones and bricks. Can be mixed by hand or mechanically on or off site.

CHECK YOUR KNOWLEDGE

1. **What three tasks can you carry out on an internal wall if you are preparing to plaster it?**

    ☐ a. Test absorbency

    ☐ b. Hack the surface

    ☐ c. Rake out mortar

    ☐ d. Brush down to remove loose materials

    ☐ e. Remove rendering

    ☐ f. Apply bonding agent

2. **True or False: Suction is the ability of a background to absorb water.**

☐ a. True

☐ b. False

3. **Which of these surfaces has medium absorbency?**

☐ a. Aircrete blocks

☐ b. Plasterboard

☐ c. Glazed tiles

4. **True or False: A mechanical key is when bonding agents such as PVA, EVA or SBR are used.**

☐ a. True

☐ b. False

Chapter 3

MATERIALS

LEARNING OBJECTIVES

By the end of this chapter you will be able to:

- List the most common materials used in plastering.

- Explain what to consider when choosing materials.

- Explain how to prepare and mix materials.

- Explain the use and safe handling of plasterboard.

- List the correct ordering, storage and disposal methods.

NOS REFERENCE

Move and handle resources

Prepare and mix plastering materials

Prepare background surfaces for plasterwork

INTRODUCTION

Choice of materials

Information about the materials will come from the specification document for the project. This will tell you about the number of coats required, the thickness of the plaster, the materials to be ordered and their quantities, and the standard of work to be achieved.

TYPES OF MATERIAL

Aggregate

Aggregate The name given to the range of particulates used in construction. These can include sand, gravel and crushed stone.

Aggregate is the name given to the range of particulates used in construction materials. These can include:

- sand
- gravel
- crushed stone.

Aggregate also includes recycled concrete. The common aggregate used in rendering is sand, although aggregates may be used in decorative finishes such as **pebble dashing**.

Pebble dashing An external render finish where pebbles or similar aggregate materials are thrown onto a fresh coat of render. Two coats are applied consisting of a scratch coat and a second, or butter, coat.

Sand

Sand is the most common aggregate used in rendering. Other aggregates may be used in decorative finishes.

The properties of sand

Sand is used as a bulking agent in rendering material; it provides an inactive and low cost bulk for the material.

The type of sand used for plastering and rendering should have a number of specific qualities. The particles of sand should be a range of different sizes to fill any gaps in the mix but none of the particles of sand should be bigger than 5mm.

The sand should be washed to remove impurities such as silt or clay (although some clay helps with the 'spreadability' of the mix). Never use soft builder's sand that is used for bricklaying. Plasterer's sand should be medium sharp. The sand should be covered when not in use to protect against contamination.

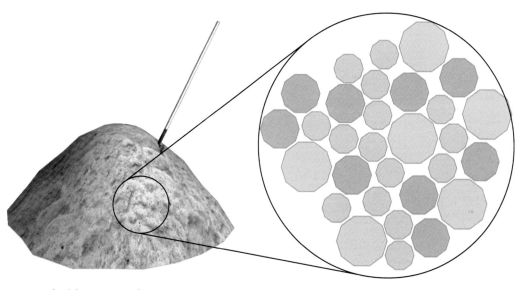

Use sand with a range of particle sizes

Sources of sand

Sand comes from a number of sources. The traditional sources include quarrying and dredging but sand produced artificially by crushing rocks and gravel is also available. Each type of sand has different characteristics and it is important to choose the right sand for plastering.

Pit sand

Pit sand is usually quarried inland. It is typically red in colour and has sharp edges.

River and sea sand

River and sea sand is dredged from the river or sea bed and is usually yellow in colour. River sand tends to be worn too smooth for internal plastering so does not stick very well. Sand from the sea contains salt which has to be washed out completely before it can be used, as any remaining salt will leave a residue on the surface later on. This residue is known as efflorescence.

Artificial sand

Artificially created sand is made by crushing stone to the relevant grade. It comes in numerous colours and is used in most modern render mixes.

Artificially created sand

Pit sand

River and sea sand

ACTIVITY

Discuss and research the qualities of plastering grade sand. Insert your findings below. What differentiates plastering sand from other types of sand?

Cement

Cement is used to bind the aggregate materials of the mix together. There are two types of cement. Hydraulic cement, such as Portland cement, uses a chemical reaction to harden. Non-hydraulic cement hardens by drying out so needs to be kept dry. Portland cement is most commonly used.

HEALTH & SAFETY

Wet cement can cause severe burns to your skin and inhaling dry cement can cause irritation to your nose and throat. Continued exposure may result in lung disease. Always wear protective clothing, gloves, eye and face protection when handling wet and dry cement.

Make sure that you gauge or measure your cement to the correct proportions, if you do not include enough cement in your mix it is likely to crumble. If you include too much the finish may crack and fall away from the wall.

Cement sets in two stages. The first stage is after 45 minutes, the second stage should be no later than 10 hours. The mix will harden after the second set as a chemical reaction between the cement and water causes hardening, the cement should therefore be cured to prevent it drying out. Cement can be cured by covering in plastic, spraying with water or covering with wet sacking.

Portland cement

Lime

Lime is used in older buildings. It is made from crushed lime-stone heated to remove carbon dioxide leaving calcium oxide. There are two types of lime:

- hydrated lime
- hydraulic lime.

Hydrated lime is made by mixing or slaking the lime with water to produce calcium hydroxide. It can be used as putty mixed with sand to create a first or **finishing coat** for interior rendering.

Hydraulic lime is made from limestone containing clay and other impurities. It can be used with sand and cement to give a flexible, breathable render.

Lime There are two types of lime, hydrated and hydraulic. They can both be used for mortar and pointing. The difference is in the setting time. The ratio for a lime mortar mix is six parts sand, one part lime and one part cement. Production and sustainability benefits make lime an eco-friendly material.

Finishing coat The final top coat in plastering, also known as setting coat or skimming coat.

HEALTH & SAFETY

Lime is an alkaline and can burn your skin. It may also affect your lungs if inhaled. Wear personal protective equipment such as gloves, protective clothing, eye and face protection.

ACTIVITY

What are the advantages of using lime as a putty or render? Explain why it is a sustainable construction product.

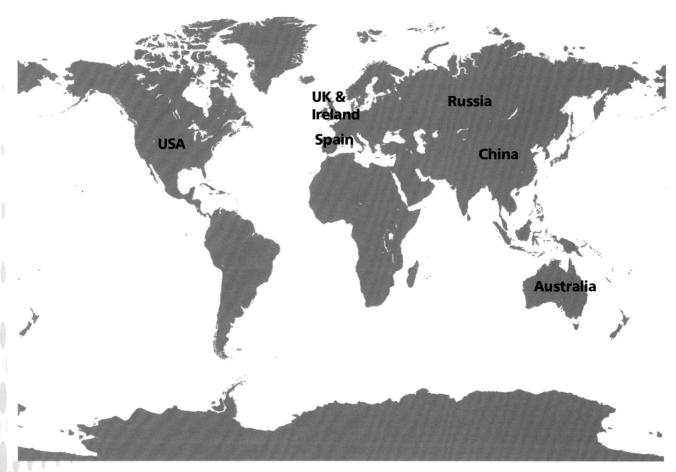

Some of the places where gypsum is found

Plaster

E-LEARNING

Use the e-learning programme to find out more about plaster.

Gypsum A type of mineral mined and quarried across the world. Usually sourced in the country where it will be used due to its low value and bulky properties. Gypsum can also be created as a by-product from other industrial processes.

Plaster is made from heating **gypsum** at high temperatures, this reduces the moisture content.

Gypsum is mined and quarried across the world. However, because it is a low value and bulky product, most gypsum is sourced in the country where it will be used. Gypsum can also be created as a by-product from other industrial processes.

HEALTH & SAFETY

When plaster is mixed with water it causes an exothermic (chemical) reaction. New crystals are created and the temperature of the mix increases and gives off heat. The temperature can get quite high so you should always take safety precautions. When the plaster sets it will have cooled down.

The setting process occurs quite quickly but can be prolonged by adding specialist **retarders**.

Plaster should be stored in a dry place off the ground. If it is allowed to get wet it will set in the bag. Always rotate the stock of plaster using the oldest plaster first. All bags of plaster will have a use by date stamped on them; check this to make sure you are using the older plaster. When new stock arrives place this behind the existing stock.

Retarder An additive used to extend the setting time of a mortar mix.

Expanded metal lathing

Expanded metal lathing or EML is a diamond shaped meshed steel and is used to cover irregular surfaces or surfaces where two different materials meet and will be plastered over. It can be made from galvanized or stainless steel for use internally or externally and can be installed over a moisture resistant backing paper.

Expanded metal lathing (EML) A diamond shaped meshed steel used to cover irregular surfaces or surfaces where two different materials meet and will be plastered over. It can be made from galvanized or stainless steel for use internally or externally.

HEALTH & SAFETY

There are a number of things to bear in mind when using EML. First of all, wear the appropriate personal protective equipment when cutting, in this case it would be gloves and goggles.

When fixing, make sure you stretch the EML tight but give it a little flexibility; otherwise the plaster will fall off. If you are using several sheets of EML overlap their edges in accordance with manufacturer's instructions and fix with ties.

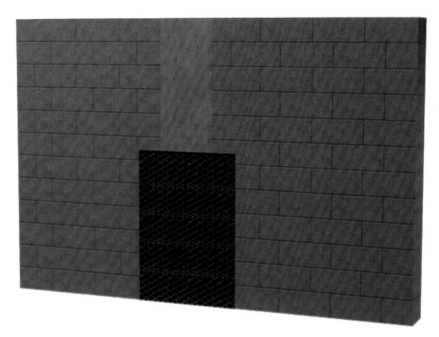

Expanded metal lath (EML)

MIXING MATERIALS

Gauging materials

When mixing materials you need to make sure that you use the correct proportions. Materials should be measured by weight or volume and containers such as buckets or gauge boxes are commonly used. Use the same container for each material needed and use the same method of measurement for the different materials.

HEALTH & SAFETY

Always make sure that you mix the proportions in a well ventilated area and wear a dust mask to avoid inhaling particles of dust.

Measure materials in the correct proportions to get the right mix

Mixing materials

There are a number of methods for mixing materials:

E-LEARNING

Use the e-learning programme to see demonstrations on mixing materials.

Mixing in a bucket

Small quantities of plaster can be mixed in a bucket. It is important that the container and tools are clean before use:

1. Add clean water into the container.
2. Add approximately 50 per cent of your plaster to the water.
3. Use your mixing drill in all directions to ensure you mix thoroughly until smooth.

4. Add in the remaining plaster and mix until you get an even consistency without any lumps.

5. Check the plaster with your trowel to make sure it's ready.

Try not to add any more water as this may weaken the mix.

Stage 1 – Add clean water

Stage 2 – Add 50% of the plaster

Stage 3 – Mix materials thoroughly

Using a cement mixer

Cement mixers are used for mixing render material.

HEALTH & SAFETY

You should always make sure you wear the correct personal protective equipment when using a cement mixer: goggles, dust mask, safety boots and gloves.

If possible plug in the cement mixer via a **residual current device (RCD)**. This is a safety cut-out device to protect you from electric shock. If you are using a petrol mixer keep the petrol away from naked flames and handle with care.

Residual current device A safety cut-out device to protect you from electric shock, recommended when using cement mixers.

Make sure the mixer is clean before use and do not overload. After you have finished make sure you clean out the drum of the mixer and drain:

1. Switch on the mixer before adding any of the materials.
2. Add clean water. If you are using a **plasticizer** add this to the water at this stage.
3. Add some of the sand, followed by the cement and lime if necessary.
4. Add the remainder of the sand and some extra water to get the right consistency.
5. Turn for at least two minutes to mix thoroughly.
6. Keep the mixer turning until everything has mixed thoroughly.
7. Be careful emptying the mixer.

> **Plasticizer** An additive that increases fluidity or plasticity of a mortar, cement paste or concrete mixture and reduces water content and drying times. Plasticizers improve the workability of a mortar mix but should not be used in structural work without the permission of the structural engineer

Stage 1 – Switch on the mixer

Stage 2 – Add clean water

Stage 3 – Add the sand and cement

Mixing by hand

E-LEARNING

Use the e-learning programme to see a demonstration of mixing by hand.

Mixing by hand should be done on a firm concrete or plywood base:

1. Place the dry materials on the board then mix on the base, turning until they are mixed thoroughly.
2. Form a well in the centre of the dry mix and add water.
3. Turn the mix into the water taking care not to allow the water to leak away.
4. Gradually add more water and continue to mix until the required consistency is achieved.
5. After the mixed material has been moved clean the base and tools well for further mixes.

Stage 1 – Place the dry materials on the board

Stage 2 – Form a well in the dry mix

Stage 3 – Turn the mix into the water

Stage 4 – Add more water and continue to mix

PLASTERBOARD

E-LEARNING

Use the e-learning programme to find out more about working with plasterboard.

Plasterboard is gypsum sandwiched between sheets of paper. It has a number of properties and can be made to different thicknesses and sizes for different areas and uses.

Plasterboard is used in a number of residential and commercial developments. It can be used to dry line masonry or timber frame external and separating walls, as partitions to separate rooms, and for mid- and top-floor ceilings.

Types of plasterboard

There are different types of plasterboard for different purposes such as sound proofing, fire and moisture resistance, thermal insulation and impact protection. Some of these are designed to meet specific building regulations.

Sound proofing

NOTE ON UK STANDARDS

Part E of the building regulations stipulates minimum noise levels for residential buildings and different types of acoustic plasterboard are available to meet these stipulations. They generally have a pale blue facing paper for easy identification.

Boards with a higher density core can be used in partition walls and ceilings between flats and houses, and plasterboard with glass mineral wool backing can be fitted in existing buildings to add an extra layer of sound proofing.

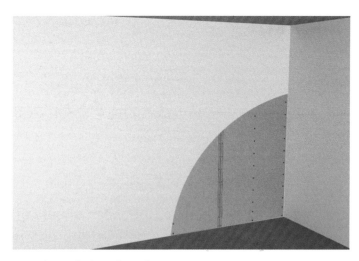

Sound proof plasterboard

Fire resistance

Additives A range of substances that can be added to mixtures to improve the strength of the mix or to control the timing in achieving the desired mix.

NOTE ON UK STANDARDS

Part B of the building regulations relates to fire safety and various types of plasterboard have been manufactured to meet these requirements. The core of the plasterboard can include glass fibre and other **additives** to give fire protection and they generally have a pink facing paper for easy identification.

Some uses of fire performance boards include fire escape routes in commercial or residential developments, lining the ceiling of a

Fire resistant plasterboard

garage integrated into a house and to enclose stairways and service ducts.

Moisture resistance

Plasterboards can have moisture resistant properties for use in areas where moisture needs to be controlled, such as bathrooms or kitchens. If you are applying a plaster skim to a moisture board then you should treat with a PVA first. Moisture performance boards generally have a green facing paper for easy identification.

Moisture resistant plasterboard

Thermal insulation

SUSTAINABILITY

Extra layers of materials such as polystyrene or foam can be added to some plasterboard to improve its thermal properties. They are made to different thicknesses for different levels of thermal performance and can be used on masonry external walls and on **cavity** walls in new homes.

Cavity The gap between the internal and external walls of a building, usually 50mm wide to increase the thermal insulation and weather resistance of the wall. The cavity must be kept clear and not bridged (except for wall ties and insulation). A damp proof course (DPC) must be provided around the perimeter of openings in cavity walls otherwise dampness can occur internally.

Thermal insulated plasterboard

Impact protection

Some plasterboards are manufactured with a higher density core for use in heavily trafficked areas such as corridors, hallways and landings.

Impact protection plasterboard

ACTIVITY

Why is plasterboard a sustainable construction product? List three reasons below.

Handling plasterboard

Working with plasterboard

When working with plasterboard you should check with the manufacturer's instructions about the board's suitability. In most cases you should fix the plasterboard with the decorative, coloured side facing out. Modern plasterboards allow for this side to be decorated or have a plaster skim applied to it. The plasterboard should have instructions written on one side.

Plasterboards also come with two different edge styles, tapered and square. Tapered edges are used for dry lining. These edges need to be filled and scrimmed and provide a smooth joint that should not show under a wall covering or paint.

Square edges are usually used when skimming over the top of the board with plaster. Again these should be scrimmed before applying any plaster.

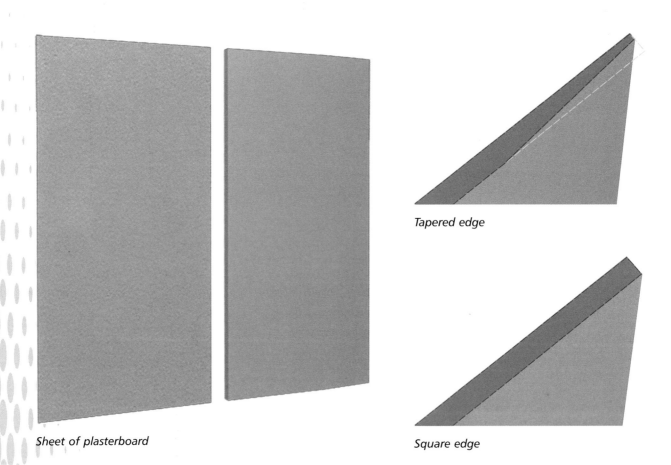

Tapered edge

Square edge

Sheet of plasterboard

ORDERING, STORING AND DISPOSING OF MATERIALS

Ordering materials

SUSTAINABILITY

It is important that only the materials required to complete the project are purchased. This will cut down on waste and keep the costs of the project under control.

When you are ordering materials for plastering you will need to consider:

- The area of surface to be covered.
- The types of surface.
- The number of coats required.
- The thickness of the coats.

MATERIALS ORDER FORM			
Order No:		**Date:**	
Site Address:			
Site Name/Address of Supplier:			
Please supply the following order to the above address:			
Description:		**Quantity:**	**Date Required:**
Special Delivery Instructions:			
Signature of Site Manager:			

Materials order form

Storing materials

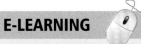

E-LEARNING

Use the e-learning programme to find out more about storing materials.

Follow manufacturer's instructions for storage of their materials. In general, keep all materials in a dry and well ventilated area and rotate the stock so that older materials are used first.

Sand

Keep sand covered with weighted tarpaulin or similar to protect against contamination. Make sure that any water can drain away from around the sand, bags should be kept in dry conditions off the ground.

Cement and plaster

If possible, store plaster and cement indoors in a dry and well ventilated space. Keep the bags away from walls and off the ground. Do not stack the bags too high, no more than five in a stack. When new stock arrives move these to the back of the old stock to ensure that the older material is used first.

Storage of bagged materials

Plasterboard

Make sure that plasterboard is stored horizontally, in a dry location and raised off the ground. Decorative faces should be together and boards should not be slid across each other as this will damage the surface.

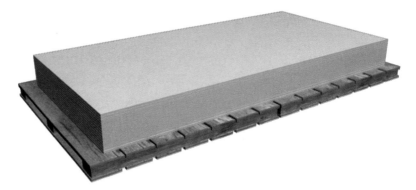

Storage of plasterboard

Disposing of and recycling materials

If you have ordered the correct amount of materials and stored and used them appropriately then there should be limited waste to dispose of. Any excess materials should be disposed of responsibly.

SUSTAINABILITY

Most building materials can be recycled, for example plasterboard. Larger construction projects will require a site waste management plan designed to reduce the amount of waste produced and the quantity that goes to landfill.

Make sure that any waste on site is stored safely and store material for recycling separately to prevent contamination. If you use a third party to remove waste make sure they are authorized to conduct their business. Do not fly tip.

CHECK YOUR KNOWLEDGE

1. **What is the maximum size for a particle of plastering sand?**

   ☐ a. 15mm

   ☐ b. 10mm

   ☐ c. 5mm

2. **What are the names of the two types of cement?**

   ☐ a. Non-hydraulic cement

   ☐ b. Hydrated cement

   ☐ c. Non-hydrated cement

   ☐ d. Hydraulic cement

3. **Match the type of plasterboard to its correct purpose by drawing an arrow to the correct description.**

Purpose

Type of plasterboard

Fire resistant plasterboard

Standard plasterboard

Moisture resistant plasterboard

Acoustic performance plasterboard

4. **True or False: Aggregate can include recycled concrete.**

☐ a. True

☐ b. False

5. **What are the two types of lime?**

☐ a. Non-hydraulic lime

☐ b. Hydraulic lime

☐ c. Hydrated lime

Chapter 4

EXTERNAL RENDERING

LEARNING OBJECTIVES

By the end of this chapter you will be able to:

- Explain what rendering is.

- List the different types of rendering.

- Describe the preparation procedures for external rendering.

- Describe the parts of render mix.

- Explain how to apply render for different types of external rendering.

INTRODUCTION

What is rendering?

Rendering is the application of materials to an external wall. The material is usually a mixture of cement and sand but could include other materials such as lime, particularly if you are working on an older building. The purpose of rendering is to provide a durable, weatherproof and aesthetically pleasing surface.

Types of rendering

E-LEARNING

Use the e-learning programme to learn more about the different types of rendering.

There are different types of external renders. The most common ones are:

- plainface
- ashlar
- pebble dashing
- tyrolean
- rough cast
- coloured cement work.

Plainface

Plainface render is the most common finish to external surfaces. It generally consists of two coats:

- a scratch coat with a water proofer additive
- a top coat.

The scratch coat is usually a stronger mix than the top coat. The top coat is applied when the scratch coat has set (around 24 hours) and should be finished with a plastic or wooden float.

Plainface render

Ashlar

Ashlar is similar to the plainface render but lines are cut into the soft finish to imitate stone blocks, the size of which can vary depending upon the surface area. An even suction is required and a waterproofing agent should be added to the scratch coat.

Set out the lines before cutting but ensure that you cut into the chalk marks as they are difficult to remove from the finish. It is a good idea to avoid placing cuts in line with sills or the **building line** as it may show up inaccuracies in the building line and will create lines that are not parallel.

Ashlar An external finish with marked lines on the plainface render to imitate stone work.

Building line One of the lines set by the local building authority; the building must not be constructed in front of this line.

Ashlar render

Pebble dashing

Pebble dashing is simply a layer of pebbles or similar aggregate material thrown onto a freshly applied coat of sand/cement. Two coats are applied:

- a scratch coat
- a second or butter coat.

The butter coat is usually applied to a thickness of 6 to 8mm but this will depend upon the size of the aggregate. It is usually applied by one plasterer as another applies the pebbles.

Pebble dash render

Tyrolean

Tyrolean is a machine finish applied to a plainface render. The material used is a plastering sand, cement and lime mix which is sprayed on the surface via a Tyrolean gun. Allow at least 24 hours for the render to dry before applying the Tyrolean finish and apply only in dry weather as damp conditions can result in a patchy appearance.

Plainface render An external render finish commonly used which generally consists of three coats: the spatterdash coat, scratch coat and floating coat.

Tyrolean finish An external render finish formed by spraying materials onto the surface using a Tyrolean gun to create a textured finish.

Tyrolean render

Rough cast

A rough cast finish is similar to pebble dashing but the pebbles or other aggregate are mixed in with the second or butter coat.

Rough cast An external render similar to pebble dashing but the pebbles or other aggregate are mixed in with the second or butter coat.

Rough cast render

Coloured cement

Most external finishes may be self-coloured but a ready-mixed coloured cement material can be used or pigments mixed in with the cement. Manufacturers now produce a variety of colouring agents that can be added to the mix. Always follow the manufacturer's instructions.

Coloured cement render

ACTIVITY

Discuss and research what type of suction background you would require for each of the finishes listed and why.

Complete the table shown below.

Type of finish	Suction required	Reason why
Plainface		
Ashlar		
Pebble dash		
Tyrolean		
Rough cast		

PREPARATION

Good preparation is vital as poor preparation could result in damp patches and fungi appearing on the inside of the wall you are rendering. There are a number of things you will need to take into consideration when preparing the background such as:

- Environmental conditions.
- The suction of the background.
- Whether you will be working at height.
- The cost of the project.
- The final appearance required.
- What type of key is required for the surface.

Parts of the render mix

Before you start work you will need to prepare the render. The render consists of three materials:

- Sand which is used as aggregate to bulk the mix.
- Cement which is used as a binder.
- An appropriate amount of plasticizer mixed with the water to make it easier to spread.

The strength of the mix goes down as the proportion of sand goes up and scratch coats should be a stronger mix than top coats. Gauge all materials accurately using the same method of measuring, use clean water to mix.

HEALTH & SAFETY

Wear the appropriate personal protective equipment: dust mask, goggles, boots, hard hat and gloves.

Proportions of render mix

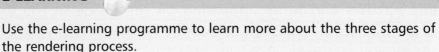

E-LEARNING

Use the e-learning programme to learn more about the three stages of the rendering process.

The proportions required for the render mix will vary depending upon the stage of the rendering process, the environmental conditions and the background surface. Not all the coats will be required in every case. Check the specification document for your project for the precise number of coats required and the proportions of render mix required for each coat.

FUNCTIONAL SKILLS

Ratios

Dubbing out layer
Very rough surfaces may require a dubbing out coat to fill holes and provide an even surface before other coats are applied. It usually consists of two parts sand to one part cement.

Scratch coat
The scratch coat is typically the first coat of render (unless a dubbing coat has been applied). The wet surface of the coat is scratched with a scratch tool to provide a key for the next coat to adhere to. The scratch coat would typically be three parts sand to one part cement.

An appropriate amount of plasticizer can be added to the water in the mix to improve workability. A waterproofing agent is used to protect the building and control suction.

Top coat
The top coat is the final coat, which will be smoothed to provide the finish. A typical ratio for top coats would be five to six parts sand to one part cement.

ACTIVITY

Identify the different coats that could be needed when rendering.

Scratch coat _____

Top coat _____

Background surface _____

Dubbing out coat _____

EXTERNAL RENDERING METHODS

Applying render

E-LEARNING

Use the e-learning programme to see a demonstration of applying render.

When applying the render mix to the surface, make sure your hawk and trowel are clean and slightly wet. This will help with the handling of the mix.

Follow these steps:

1. Use your trowel to put the mix onto your hawk.
2. Hold the trowel on your hawk at about 70° and push forward.
3. At the same time move your hawk from level to about 110°.
4. This transfers some of the mix from the hawk to the trowel.
5. If you are right-handed, start at the top left corner and sweep. If you are left-handed, start at the top right corner.

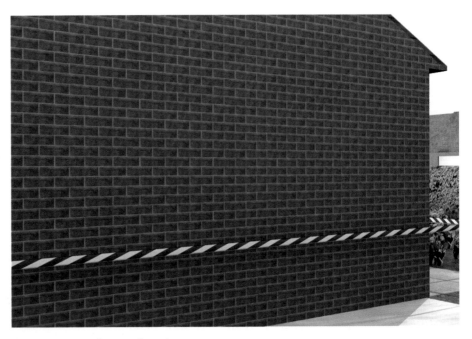

Prepare your surface and work area

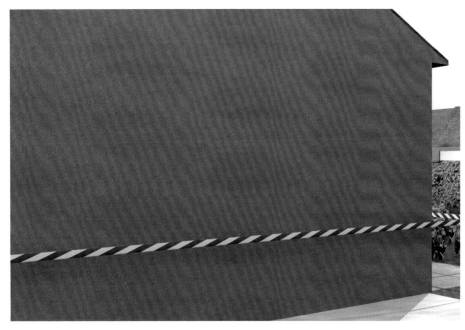

Use your hawk and trowel

Apply render materials

6. Sweep upwards and to the right. Start with your trowel at 45°. As you go higher, reduce the angle of the trowel.

7. Put a small amount of material on your trowel and sweep in from the edge.

8. Once you have covered the surface, clean and flatten any high spots using your trowel.

Applying the scratch coat

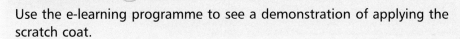

E-LEARNING

Use the e-learning programme to see a demonstration of applying the scratch coat.

The scratch coat is applied evenly. It should be scored horizontally with a wave like motion using a scratching tool. Cross scoring will weaken the coat. The score will retain the water sprayed on the surface to help it cure. You should avoid scoring too deep as this will create holes in the coat and make it not waterproof.

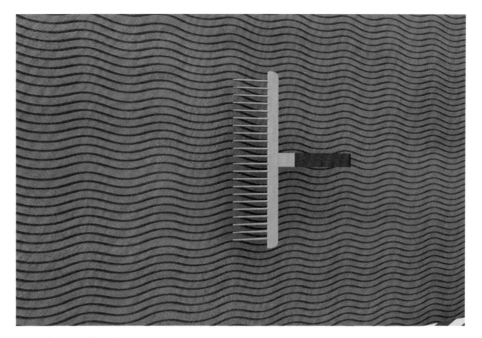

Score in one direction

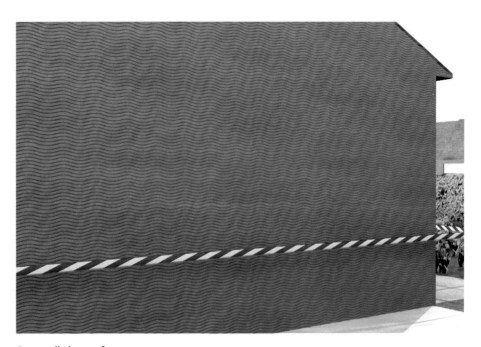

Score all the surface

Applying the top coat

E-LEARNING

Use the e-learning programme to see a demonstration of applying the top coat.

Allow 24 hours for the scratch coat to set before applying the top coat. Once you have applied the render mix rule over the entire surface using a straight edge or Darby to a flat finish.

Wait for the surface to set slightly before consolidating or rubbing up the surface with a wooden or plastic float. Finish with a lightly applied sponge to smooth the surface.

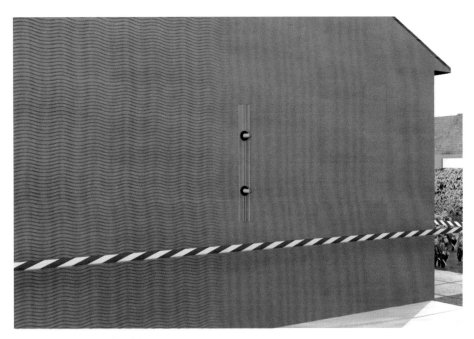

Rule the surface flat

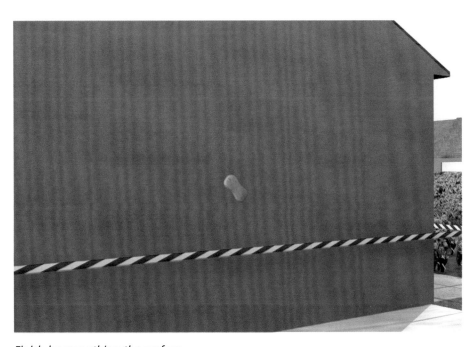

Finish by smoothing the surface

Making an Ashlar finish

E-LEARNING

Use the e-learning programme to see a demonstration of making an Ashlar finish.

An Ashlar finish is a series of lines drawn into the top coat to create a block effect:

1. Mark a horizontal line and plumb two vertical lines on the top coat.

> **Course** A row of bricks, concrete blocks, etc. in a wall.

2. Mark the height of each block **course** on the vertical lines.

3. Cut the horizontal joints.

4. Mark the block lengths along the horizontal joints and cut these in.

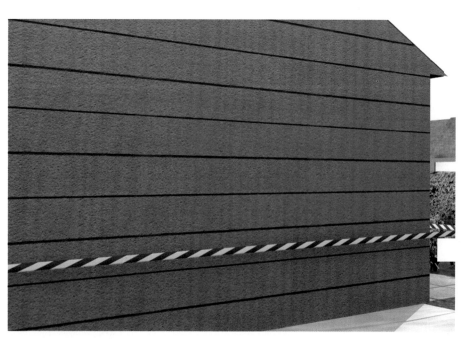

Mark horizontal lines

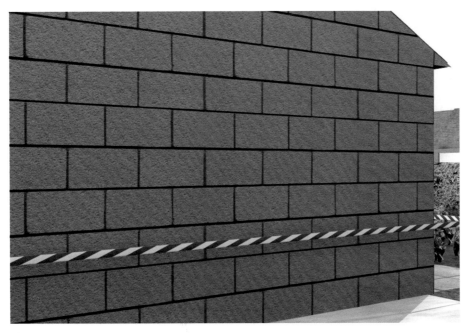

Mark vertical lines

Pebble dashing

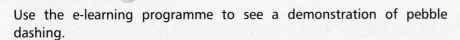

E-LEARNING

Use the e-learning programme to see a demonstration of pebble dashing.

Pebble dashing is a two-person job. One plasterer applies the top or butter coat whilst the other applies the pebbles.

- Place a sheet at the base of the wall to catch pebbles which drop to the ground.
- Make sure the pebbles are of a similar grade and from the same batch.
- Use a dashing paddle to throw the pebbles at 90° to the wall.
- Any other angle will result in an uneven appearance.
- Do not pat the pebbles into the surface.
- After use wash and save pebbles for later use.

Pebble dashing a wall

Tyrolean finish

The Tyrolean finish should be applied after the plainface render has dried and only in dry conditions to avoid a patchy appearance.

Before starting, mask up all doors and windows to protect them. Apply three coats:

● The first coat from the left at an angle of 45° to the wall.

● The second coat from the right at the same angle.

● Apply a final coat straight at the wall.

● Make sure you keep the Tyrolean gun moving at all times.

Tyrolean render finish

First coat at 45 degrees from the left

Second coat at 45 degrees from the right

Final coat straight on

Applying beading

Beading is used to protect render where surfaces meet at an angle, to provide a stop for render at edges and openings, and to provide a bellcast to protect against rain. Beading typically comes in 2400mm and 3000mm lengths. For external work use plastic or stainless steel beading, for internal work, galvanized steel or plastic is used.

Examples of beading

Angle beads

Angle beads are used for all external angles around corners and windows. Use a spirit level to check that the bead is vertical and fix in place with dabs of plaster.

Stop beads

Stop beads are used to create a neat completion of render work and to protect the edge of the render; they can also be used to create expansion joints. Stop beads are generally fixed using masonry nails.

Spirit level A tool used to check true vertical and horizontal lines indicated by a bubble in spirit-filled vials.

Bellcast beads

Stainless steel bellcast bead/render stop beads are used over window and door openings and above the dampproof course for external renders. External render stop bead or bellcast beads can be used to form and protect the lower edge of render, to form a bellcast over a door or window which will divert the rain water from the opening and to form a finish for the render at the bottom of a wall above the damp proof course.

Damp proof course (DPC) A horizontal layer of impervious materials such as bituminous felt, asphalt, two courses of slate or two courses of engineering bricks. It is usually laid at 150mm above ground level to prevent moisture rising. A damp proof course is also used for walls subject to high compressive loads. It is also necessary to form an impervious barrier in cavity walls when bridging openings (e.g. doors and windows).

FUNCTIONAL SKILLS

Ratios

CHECK YOUR KNOWLEDGE

1. **You have been asked to apply a scratch coat at a ratio of 3:1. Each bag of cement weighs 25kg. How many kg of sand are required for each bag of cement?**

2. **True or False: A scratch coat applied to a wall should be scored vertically.**

    ☐ a. True

    ☐ b. False

3. **True or False: Ashlar is a type of external render.**

    ☐ a. True

    ☐ b. False

4. **Which coat of render would be the final coat?**

    ☐ a. Dubbing out layer

    ☐ b. Scratch coat

    ☐ c. Top coat

Chapter 5

INTERNAL PLASTERING

LEARNING OBJECTIVES

By the end of this chapter you will be able to:

- List the different types of internal plastering.

- Identify the tools needed.

- List the materials required.

- Explain the process for applying material to walls, ceilings and floors.

- Explain how to fit plasterboard to walls and ceilings.

- Explain fibrous plasterwork.

- Know what final checks to carry out.

Fibrous plasterwork
Decorative plasterwork that is usually made off-site.

We will also look at **fibrous plasterwork** and what to check for when the work is concluded.

NOS REFERENCE

Prepare background surfaces for plasterwork

Produce internal solid plastering finishes

Install direct bond dry linings

Confirm the occupational method of work

Position and secure plasterwork resources

Lay sand and cement screeds

Position and secure fibrous plaster components

Confirm work activities and resources for the work

INTRODUCTION

Preparation of the working area

Before you start work it is important you have prepared the working area to ensure that property is protected from damage and that the work is carried out safely.

HEALTH & SAFETY

Make sure that the work area is made safe and members of the public and other workers are protected. Remove or cover any objects and sheet up the floors including those into the room in which you are working.

WALLS

Number of coats

Depending on the type of work to be carried out and the background surface, internal plastering can consist of up to three coats. On very rough surfaces an extra dubbing out coat is also applied before the render coat to fill hollows.

Skim coat – plasterboard

E-LEARNING

Use the e-learning programme to see a skim coat in more detail.

A skim coat is a finish coat around 2 to 3mm deep. It is usually applied to plasterboard or other sheet materials and is applied in stages.

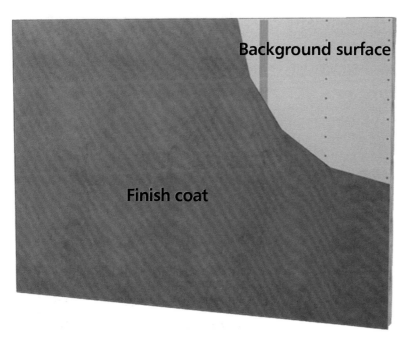

Skim coat

Two coat work

Two coat work or float and set consists of two coats, an under-coat or **floating coat** and a finish coat. It is applied to solid backgrounds such as brickwork and blockwork.

> **Floating coat** A backing coat which provides a surface for the final coat, known as the finishing, setting or skimming coat.

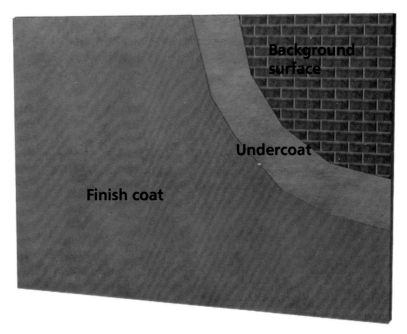

Two coat work

Three coat work

Three coat work, or render, float and set consists of three coats:

- two undercoats
- finishing coat.

The first undercoat is a render or scratch coat which applies suction and stiffens up the background. The second coat is called a floating coat and the final coat is known as finishing coat, **setting coat** or **skimming coat**. It is used on surfaces that have EML installed (see Chapter 3).

ACTIVITY

What are the different coats known as in three coat work? Label the diagram shown.

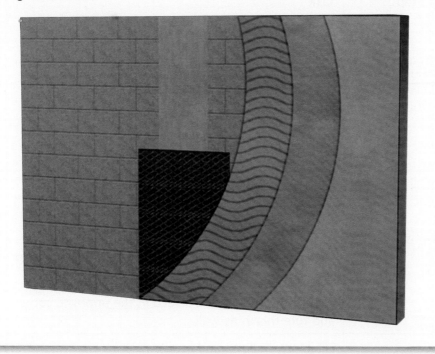

Setting coat The final top coat in plastering also known as finishing coat or skimming coat.

Skimming coat The final top coat in plastering also known as finishing coat or setting coat.

Applying the floating coat

Floating coats are usually applied using the following methods:

Box screed method

E-LEARNING

Use the e-learning programme to see a demonstration of the box screed method.

Screed A narrow band of material used as a guide when applying plaster undercoats.

The box **screed** method is typically used in smaller areas. It does not give the highest quality surface but it is more accurate than working freehand.

ACTIVITY

How do you think the box screed method is carried out? Put the following steps in the correct order by labelling them Step 1 to Step 9.

Step	Task
	Rule over the screed in an up and down movement until it is at a thickness of approximately 11mm.
	Lay the rule on the middle of one of the vertical screeds and keeping the rule level, rule off the material until it lies flat with the horizontal screed.
	Rule in these screeds to the same thickness as the vertical screeds.
	Fill in between the screeds and rule off.
	Now apply two horizontal screeds at about 25mm above the floor and just below the ceiling.
	Apply a vertical screed of plaster to the surface near the corner.
	Apply a second vertical screed in the opposite corner and rule this in as well.
	Fill in any hollows and re-rule.
	Lay the rule on the middle of one of the vertical screeds and keeping the rule level, rule off the material until it lies flat with the horizontal screed.

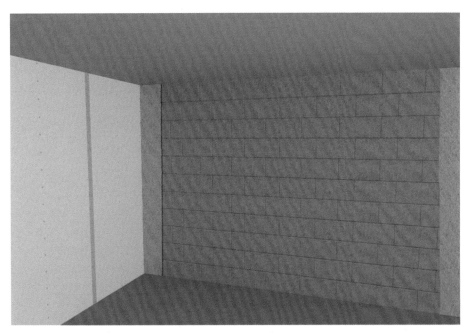

Apply vertical screeds and level

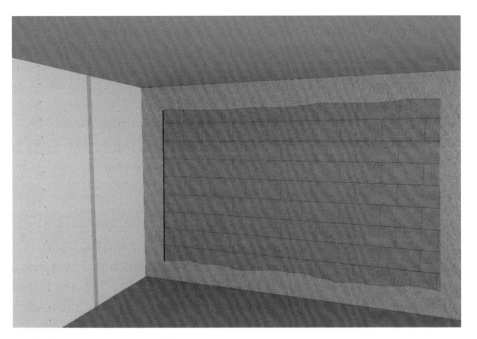

Apply horizontal screeds and level

Fill in between screeds

Dot and screed method

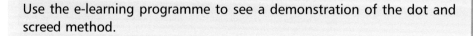

E-LEARNING

Use the e-learning programme to see a demonstration of the dot and screed method.

The dot and screed method, also known as the plumb and dot method, is used in two or three coat work for larger areas and where an absolutely plumb surface is required. A dot is a small piece of wood on a dab of plaster.

ACTIVITY

How do you think the dot and screed method is carried out? Put the following steps in the correct order by labelling them Step 1 to Step 9.

Step	Task
	Join the dots together as per the box screed system.
	Line through the intermediate dots horizontally off the four main dots.
	Place a dot near the top of the wall.
	Add additional dots between the two main ones above each other.
	Remove the dots and infill then fill in between screeds and rule off.
	Plumb in the two dots with a floating rule. If you were doing this on a very large wall you could use a **plumb bob** or a **laser level**.
	Place a third and fourth dot at the other end of the wall and plumb these in.
	Place a second dot lower down the wall.
	Check them for plumb with the lower dots.

Plumb bob A weight attached to the plumb line, for checking vertical lines and providing a guide for constructing gable end walls.

Laser level A mechanical device mounted on a stand which extends to the height of the room. The laser level projects the horizontal and vertical levels onto the surface using laser beams.

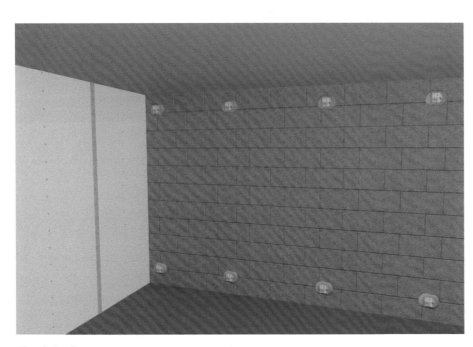

Plumb in dots

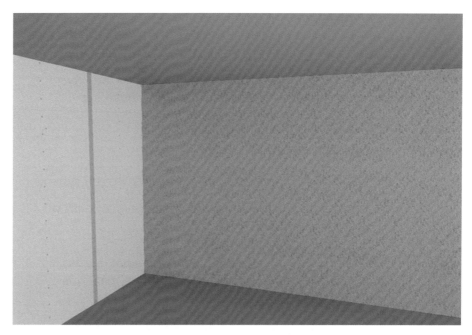

Remove dots and fill in remaining area

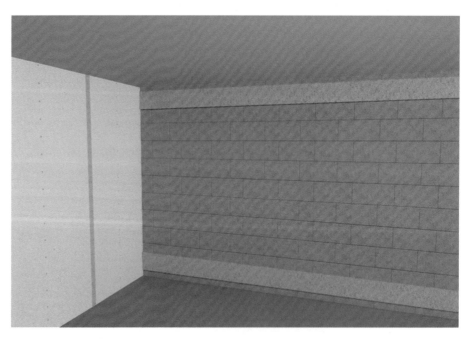

Join dots with a screed

Applying the finishing coat

E-LEARNING

Use the e-learning programme to see a demonstration of applying the finishing coat

The finishing coat is a finer layer of plaster that's applied to the surface to give it a flat and smooth finish.

ACTIVITY

How do you think the finishing coat is applied? Put the following steps in order by labelling them Step 1 to Step 6.

Step	Task
	Start from the top left of the wall (or top right if you are left-handed) and apply the plaster across the top section of the wall.
	Allow the first coat to pick up slightly before applying the second coat in the same way (the second coat is called the laying down coat). The laying down coat will use less material than the first coat. Once you have applied the laying down coat move to the trowelling up stage to finish the surface off.
	To avoid contamination from earlier mixes make sure that the bucket and mixing tools are clean before use and clean them immediately after use.
	Make sure the wall is prepared before the mixing takes place.
	The water used for the mix should be clean and cold.
	If the wall is high fill in the middle section next and then finish at the bottom using upward strokes.

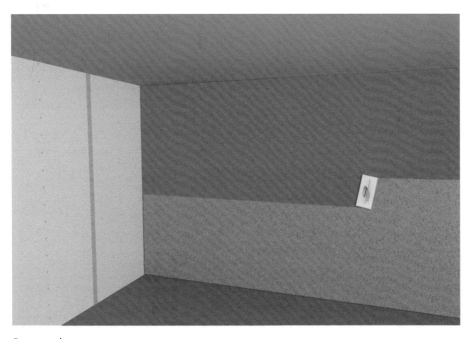

Start at the top

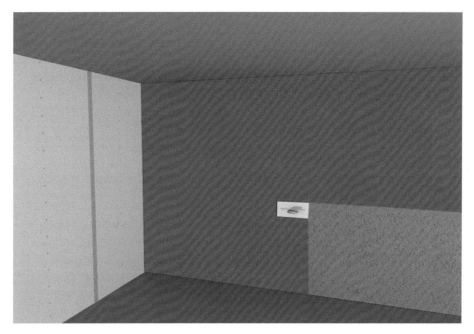

Finish at the bottom

E-LEARNING

Use the e-learning programme to see a demonstration of the trowelling up stage.

The trowelling up stage is the final stage of finishing off the wall following applying the first and laying down coats.

ACTIVITY

What do you think is involved in the trowelling up stage? Put the following steps in order by labelling them Step 1 to Step 3.

Step	Task
	As the wall sets, trowel the surface lightly. Begin at the same point you applied the first coat. Apply a small amount of water at this stage.
	Clean off all the angles. If you use a brush avoid leaving brush marks on the surface. Apply a final trowel to the wall to finish it off.
	Flatten the surface with a clean dry trowel.

Trowel up using some of these tools

Fixing angles

E-LEARNING

Use the e-learning programme to see a demonstration of fixing angles.

Angles can either be formed where you use the plaster to create the edge or fixed where beading is applied. The latter is most common in plastering today.

ACTIVITY

How do you think you fix an angle bead? Put the following steps in order by labelling them Step 1 to Step 6.

Step	Task
	Make sure that the beading is straight and is plumb on both sides of the angle.
	Check the wall is plumb.
	Apply material to both sides of the bead and check again that its plumb.
	Apply a line of plaster dabs along the angle and press the bead into the dabs.
	Cut the beading to size using snips.
	Clean up the bead.

Check the wall is plumb

Fix angle bead

Apply material over the bead

WORKING WITH PLASTERBOARD

Cutting plasterboard

When fitting plasterboard you will need to plan the room to make sure you know what sizes are required and to avoid wastage. In some cases you will need to cut the boards to fit part of the room.

Plasterboard is usually cut 15mm shorter than the height of the room so that it doesn't touch the ground although it is always best to check this against the building specification document depending on the type of board used. You will also need to take into consideration any socket boxes or switches that might be present.

The tools required for cutting plasterboard include:

- Tape measure
- Straight edge
- Sharp knife or plasterboard saw
- Rasp or surform.

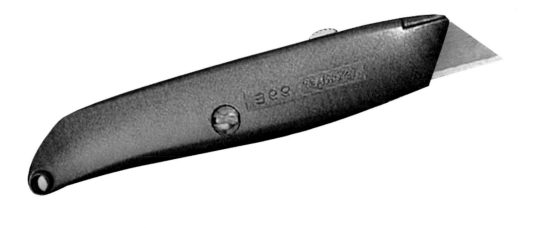

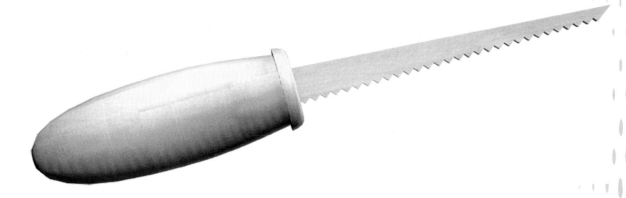

Some of the tools used when cutting plasterboard

Trimming plasterboard

E-LEARNING

Use the e-learning programme to see a demonstration of trimming plasterboard.

To trim plasterboard:

1. Use a straight edge and trimming knife to cut through the face paper but not into the core of the plasterboard.
2. Turn the board over and bend to snap open the cut.
3. Cut through the paper on the other side to finish.
4. Use the rasp or surform to smooth the cut edge.

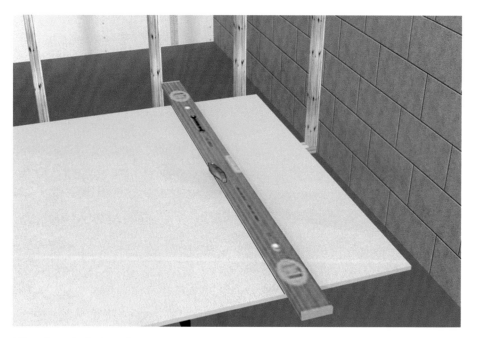

Trimming plasterboard

Cutting smaller openings

E-LEARNING

Use the e-learning programme to see a demonstration of cutting smaller openings.

Stud wall An internal, non-load-bearing timber-frame wall faced with lath and plaster or plasterboard.

When fitting plasterboard you will need at some stage to cut out openings for electrical socket boxes and light switches. If you are fitting the boards to a **stud wall** then the socket boxes and switches are likely to already be installed so you can fix the board in place then cut out the hole. In some cases you may need to measure where the opening will be and mark out the dimensions on the board before fixing in place.

To cut out the hole:

1. Mark the area and use a pad saw which has a very sharp edge to create the initial opening.
2. Saw around the marking.
3. Smooth the edges with a rasp or surform.

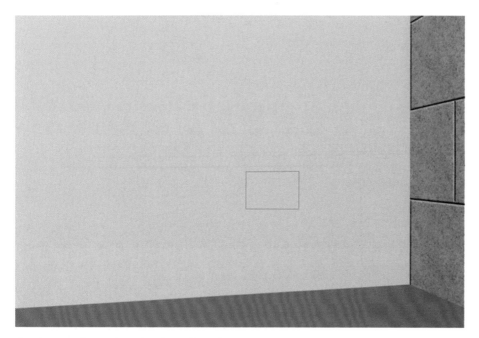

Cutting small openings in plasterboard

Cutting larger openings

E-LEARNING

Use the e-learning programme to see a demonstration of cutting larger openings.

If you are plasterboarding around an opening such as a window or a doorway you will need to cut the board to fit.

This can be done two ways by either cutting it before it's fitted or once it's in place. You can use the opening or a straight edge as a guide. Use a plasterboard saw to cut the horizontal line first until you get to the edge of the opening, and then use a Stanley knife to cut the vertical line starting from the top and working your way down.

Fix the board in place

Mark area to cut

Cut horizontally then vertically

Fixing plasterboard

You can fit plasterboard using two methods:

- Method 1 – Dry lining which is fixing the plasterboard to a solid wall using a dry wall **adhesive**.
- Method 2 – Fixing the plasterboard to metal or timber frame such as stud walls.

Adhesive General term given to a range of bonding agents.

With either method you need to take into consideration the starting point and any openings. If there are no openings then start at the internal corner, otherwise start at the opening. Fixing plasterboard around an opening can be done in two different ways:

- One method is to fix the plasterboard over the opening and cut off the excess board using the doorway as a guide.
- The other method is to cut the plasterboard shorter and have a horizontal board extending beyond the vertical studs of the opening.

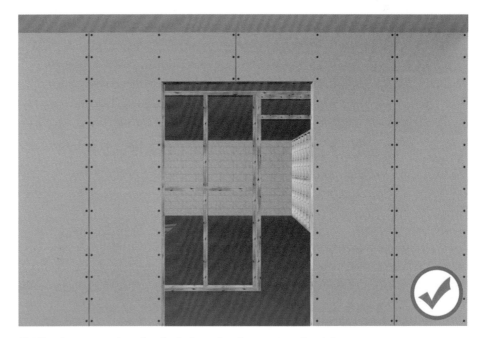

Cutting large openings in plasterboard – doorway method 1

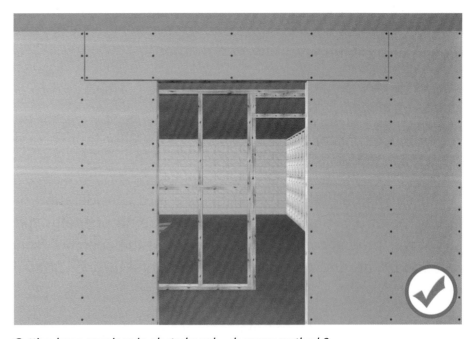

Cutting large openings in plasterboard – doorway method 2

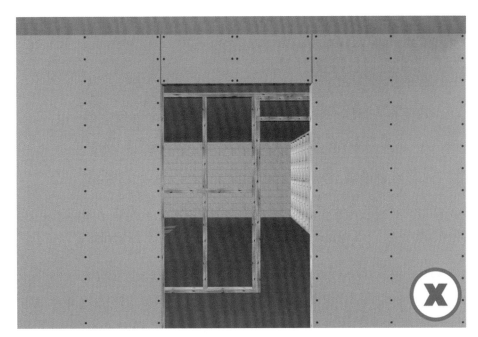

Cutting large openings in plasterboard – doorway method 2

The important thing to remember is not to have joints in line with the door frame as it could lead to damage from the forces of the door opening and closing.

ACTIVITY

Discuss the reasons for where and how you should position, cut and fix plasterboard around openings. Write your reasons below.

Fixing to solid walls (dry lining)

E-LEARNING

Use the e-learning programme to see a demonstration of fixing to solid walls.

If you are attaching plasterboard direct to the wall using the dot and dab method then first check your wall is plumb.

1. Mark out a line on the floor where the boards will line up and transfer this to the ceiling using a straight edge and a spirit level.

2. You will need to plan the size of boards needed for the wall.

3. Starting from a corner mark out the required board sizes on the wall, usually 1200mm wide for a full board, although they can also come in other sizes.

4. After marking out, mix up your dry wall adhesive with a drill whisk to the consistency of a stiff finish plaster.

5. Apply continuous lines of this dry wall adhesive with your hawk and trowel to the **perimeter** of the wall.

6. Where your first board is going to be placed, apply dots of the dry wall adhesive approximately 50 to 75mm wide by 250mm long and 30 to 35mm thick in three vertical rows leaving approximately 75mm between each.

7. The dabs on each side should be at least 25mm inside where the edge of the board will be so the joint isn't breached.

8. Now that your adhesive is in place, position the board with the grey side facing the wall against the dabs, with the bottom resting on some support material.

9. Use a straight edge to push the board against the adhesive and the wall, lining the board up with the floor and ceiling lines.

10. Use a foot lifter to push the board tight against the ceiling.

11. Wipe off any excess adhesive with a damp sponge. Repeat this process for the remaining wall space making sure the boards have a slight gap between them, usually about 2–4mm.

Perimeter The total length of the boundary to a closed shape, e.g. a room inside a building.

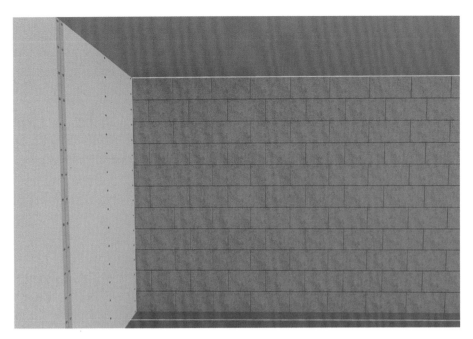

Mark out ceiling and floor lines

Apply adhesive to wall

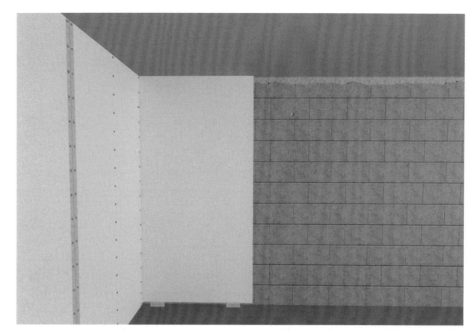

Position and fix plasterboard

ACTIVITY

Draw on the diagram where you should apply your dots of dry wall adhesive when fixing plasterboard to solid walls.

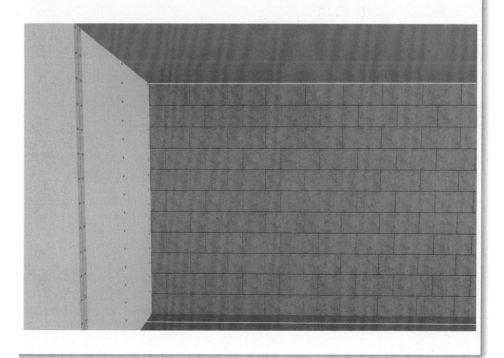

Fixing plasterboard to a frame

E-LEARNING

Use the e-learning programme to see a demonstration of fixing to a frame.

Whether you are fixing plasterboard to a timber or metal frame stud wall, or a frame attached to a solid wall, the process is very similar.

The vertical studs of the frame are usually positioned 400, 450 or 600mm apart. Plasterboard tends to be fitted vertically but on some occasions can be fitted horizontally. In this situation **noggings** have to be fitted between the studs to provide support.

Plan out the wall to see how many boards you are going to need. You may need to cut boards to fit, but remember the edges must be supported. Use a **footlifter** to help you position the boards.

Place the board with the grey side facing inwards and make sure the edges are placed half way over the vertical studs. Galvanized nails or dry wall screws are commonly used and these are usually spaced 300mm apart. If the board spans vertical studs between the edges, then the board should be fixed to these studs as well. The thickness of the board will affect the length of the fixing required and remember not to fracture the paper of the board when fixing. Boards should be positioned with a gap of 2–3mm between them.

Noggings Short horizontal timber struts fitted between studs in a timber stud wall.

Footlifter A metal tool used for holding a tacked down plasterboard in place whilst it's being fixed.

Plan out the amount of plasterboard needed

Plasterboard edges need to be fixed to timber studs

Finishing plasterboard

Once the plasterboard has been fitted you need to finish it off for decorating or skimming.

Decorating plasterboard – taping and jointing

If you are decorating the plasterboard you are likely to have used tapered edge boards and there a number of steps you will need to carry out before the boards are ready:

1. Secure self-adhesive scrim tape over the centre of the vertical joint, always place tape edges next to each other rather than overlapping.
2. Apply two or three layers of jointing compound to the joint, feathering out each layer so it's wider than the previous.
3. Leave each layer to set fully and sand to a smooth finish before adding the next coat.

You will also need to apply the jointing compound over each screw hole and again sand to a smooth finish. Complete the process by applying a sealing agent to the boards.

Jointing The process of finishing off mortar joints in brickwork or blockwork to waterproof the wall. Timing is crucial for jointing as the mortar may crumble if jointing is carried out after the mortar has dried.

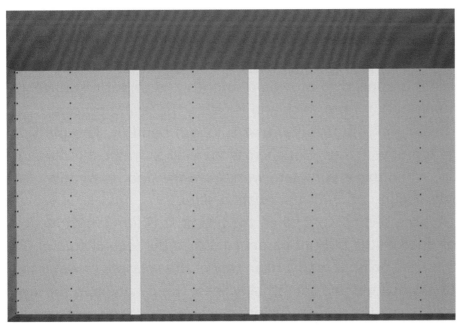

Use tape and joint filler on plasterboard joins and screw heads

Leave filler to dry at every stage

Skimming plasterboard

If you are applying a plaster skim over the plasterboard then you are likely to have used square edge boards which just need a self-adhesive scrim tape placed over the joints before skimming.

When the plasterboard is in place and prepared, a thin coat of plaster is applied to provide a smooth and uniform surface. It is usually about 3mm thick and is called the laying on coat.

Begin with a horizontal trowel length band of skim plaster at the top of wall then work across the wall from the middle to the top. When this is complete work from the floor to middle of the wall meeting up with the existing skim.

Apply a second coat when the first coat is firm which means it has dried a little but not hardened. When the second coat of plaster is firm, polish it with a clean trowel and splashes of water to fill out any hollows and smooth any lines. This is known as the laying down coat. Do not apply too much water – you just want to moisten, not saturate the plaster.

Start at the top

Finish at the bottom

CEILINGS

Working at height

You will need to consider your safety and the safety of others around you when working at height. The platform or scaffolding that you are working on should be set at the correct height. This is usually determined by having a 100mm gap from the top of the plasterer's head to the ceiling.

HEALTH & SAFETY

You should also ensure there are no gaps or traps in the scaffold, the supports are set at the correct span for the scaffold you are using and guard rails are in place. Wear appropriate personal protective equipment.

Fixing plasterboard to a ceiling

Plasterboard placed on a ceiling should be well supported. Boards should be fixed with the grey side facing the ceiling and tacked in place with galvanized nails or drywall screws, with their heads just below the surface without fracturing the paper.

1. Starting from the corner of the room, fix the cut edge of the boards half way along the joists.

2. Boards should not be over hanging the edge of a joist. You should leave a small gap between boards, approximately 2 to 4mm and boards need to be staggered to avoid any weak points.

3. After attaching all the boards to the ceiling, use self-adhesive tape over the joints. Ceilings without coving or cornice will require tape on the joint between wall and ceiling.

4. You should try to plaster the boards as soon as possible to avoid any dust clogging the pores of the plasterboard.

Coving A curved moulding at the junction between the walls and ceiling of a room—a form of cornice.

Start in the corner

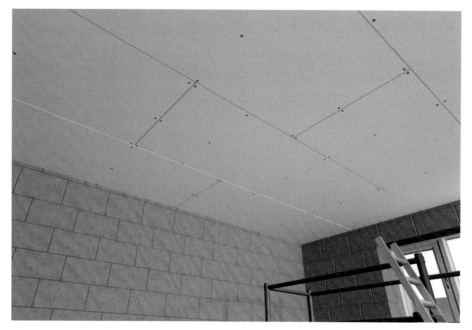

Stagger the plasterboard so that no joins meet

Tape over joints

HEALTH & SAFETY

Make sure you are wearing your goggles, dust mask and gloves.

Applying a ceiling finishing coat

HEALTH & SAFETY

Before applying a finishing coat to the ceiling make sure the scaffolding or raised platform is properly in place and that the surface has been prepared correctly as described earlier in this section.

The room should be as empty as possible and your tools and materials close at hand. There is a set process to finishing a ceiling and you should work to the same method when applying the plaster.

E-LEARNING

Use the e-learning programme to see more information on applying a ceiling finishing coat.

The mix

Mix a finish plaster that's suitable for the surface to a consistency that's firm but not too firm. As always, mix in clean water using a drill whisk.

HEALTH & SAFETY

You are going to be plastering above your head so it needs to stick to the ceiling but not be so firm that you can't apply it without straining your shoulder, arm and neck.

Laying on coat

E-LEARNING

Use the e-learning programme to see a demonstration of applying the laying on coat.

The first coat is known as the laying on coat and is usually 2–3mm thick. This particular method works by applying the plaster in decreasingly sized squares.

1. Begin in a corner; right-handed plasterers usually start in the left corner and vice versa.

2. Apply the plaster in long smooth strokes along the wall line, bringing the trowel over your shoulder.

3. Continue this process until you have completed a lap of the room and end up at your initial starting point.

4. Begin another lap inside the previous one and continue this process until you have a small square left in the middle of the room.

5. Once the ceiling is covered, clean down your tools and flatten any lines in the plaster.

Start in the same place each time

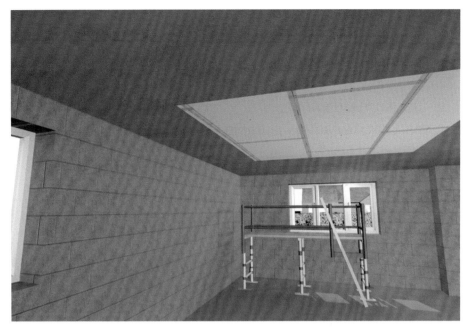

Work in decreasing size areas

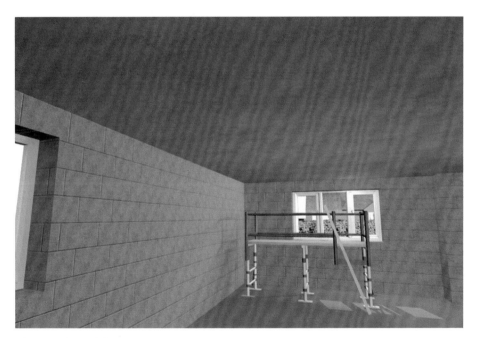

Clean tools and flatten lines

Laying down coat

E-LEARNING

Use the e-learning programme to see a demonstration of applying the laying down coat.

When the laying on coat is firm to touch you are ready to put on the laying down coat. This is a thinner mix, approximately a third of what you mixed previously for the laying on coat.

Start at the same point as before and use the same method to apply the laying down coat, finishing in the same spot. Try to keep this coat as neat as possible.

Trowelling up

E-LEARNING

Use the e-learning programme to see a demonstration of trowelling up.

As the plaster sets or picks up and is again firm to touch you can begin the final, trowelling up stage.

Timing is crucial here as if you start too soon the plaster may bubble, but start too late and the plaster will be too hard to work with. Again starting in the same place and using the same method use a clean dry trowel to fill any hollows and clear any lines. You may need to add a splash of water here and there, just enough to help move the trowel smoothly over the surface. You can repeat this process two or three times to ensure a good finish.

FLOORS

Floor screed The final layer of concrete laid on top of the oversite concrete to level off. The floor screed is usually laid later on in the project.

Tools and equipment for surfacing floors

You will use a number of tools and equipment when laying **floor screeds**.

ACTIVITY

The tools listed here can be used when laying floor screeds. Can you complete their names?

C_M_N_ _X_
_U C_T
B_IL_ER'S _Q_A_E
_P A_E
_T_R_L_L
S_IT_ VE_
FL_ RT_ W_
G_ G_NG_ RO_L
_PE_EA_R_
_H_ KL_ E
R U_

HEALTH & SAFETY

Ensure you wear the appropriate PPE at all times.

Materials

The two main components of materials for floor screeding are sand and **ordinary Portland cement**.

The sand should be sharp sand with larger angular grains of sand. It should be free from impurities. The proportions for the mix is usually either three parts of sand to one part of cement or four parts of sand to one part of cement.

Ordinary Portland cement One of the raw ingredients of mortar, made from crushed limestone or clay mixed with water which is then heated at very high temperatures and ground into a powder form.

ACTIVITY

Use the internet to research the differences between plasterer's sand and flooring sand. Write your findings below.

Types of floor screed

Bonded floor screed

The bonded screed is laid directly onto a concrete surface which has had a mix of cement slurry and PVA applied to it. The surface will be ruled in a rough state with the aggregate showing to help the flooring bond. The bonded screed should be approximately 38mm thick.

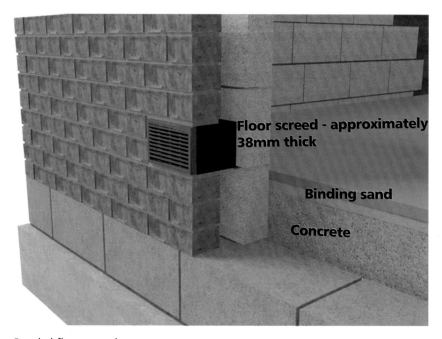

Floor screed - approximately 38mm thick

Binding sand

Concrete

Bonded floor screed

Unbonded floor screed

The unbonded screed is laid onto a damp proof membrane which is situated on top of the concrete sub-base. It should be a minimum thickness of 75mm.

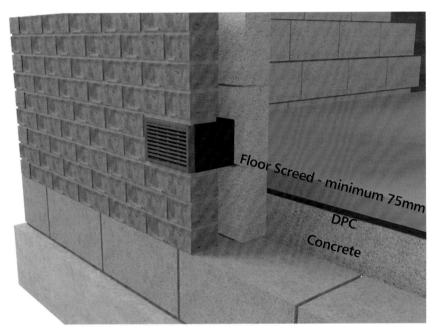

Unbonded floor screed

Floating floor screed

The floating floor screed is laid over insulation boards. It is between 65 to 100mm thick depending on whether the building is a commercial or residential unit.

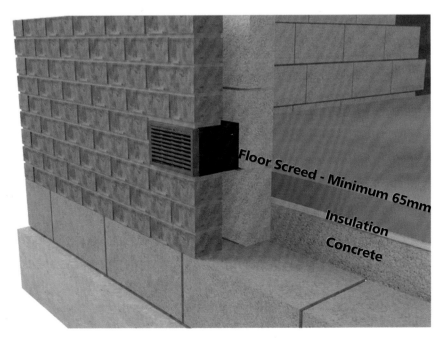

Floating screed

WEBLINKS

ACTIVITY

Investigate which of the floor screeds offer the most sustainable and environmental benefits and why. Write your findings below.

Laying floor screeds

E-LEARNING

Use the e-learning programme to see a demonstration of laying a floor screed.

When laying floor screeds begin by checking the floor level. This can be done by taking a level from a datum point or fixed point. The datum point is usually worked out and marked in advance on the site. The second method is to take the level from the bottom of a door frame or similar.

1. Lay a screed on the floor surface approximately 300mm in depth, consolidate or compact the screed well and use a builder's square to check the accuracy of the screed against the datum line or against the level of the door frame.

2. Spread out the material on the floor between the screeds.

3. Rule backwards and forward to bring level with the screeds.

4. Check for level by laying a spirit level diagonally across the top.

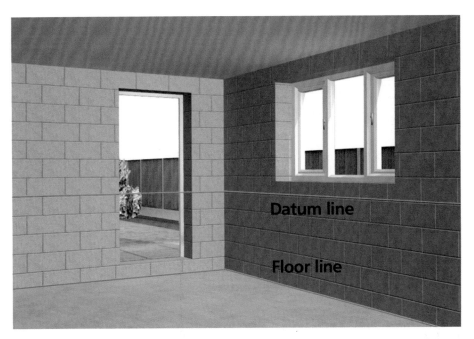

Check floor level

Lay a line of screed

Complete floor screed

Check for level

Floor finishes

There are three types of finish to the face of the floor screed:

The trowel finish created with a flooring trowel gives a reasonably smooth surface and is used if only a thin type of floor covering is to be used.

A float finish is completed with a large float and is appropriate if the surface is to be covered in wooden block or similar.

The final type of finish is a latex finish or smoothing compound or self-levelling compound. It is a mix of cement, silver sand and glue additives trowelled thinly onto a finished surface. It leaves a smooth finish.

Levelling The process of using a spirit level to check and mark levels.

Curing floors

Once the floor has been finished try to keep people away from the area for around seven days to give it time to cure or harden.

There are two methods of controlling the curing. One is to cover the floor with a plastic sheet and allow it to sweat under the cover for around seven days. Spray with a little water to help the floor cure. The surface should be hard in about seven days.

Curing The method of preventing the loss of water in concrete foundation by slowing the chemical reaction of hydration, as the strength of the concrete cannot be maximized if it is dried too quickly. Curing usually takes up to seven days and there are a number of ways concrete can be cured including covering with damp hessian or polythene sheets or spraying the concrete with a curing compound. However, during cold weather the hessian should be dry to prevent frosting.

Cure with a plastic sheet

Alternatively, spray a chemical curing agent onto the floor surface. After a number of days, this will break down and leave the face free of any curing agent.

Cure with a chemical agent

FIBROUS PLASTERWORK

Fibrous plasterwork

Fibrous plasterwork is decorative plasterwork which is usually made off-site before fitting. It is made of gypsum plaster reinforced with hessian or similar materials.

Various techniques are used to create the plasterwork. A typical method is the running mould to create objects such as moulding that run around walls. Once the plasterwork has been created it will need to be fitted in place.

Hessian A coarse fabric used to cover the concrete foundations during the curing process.

Creating a panel moulding

There are two stages to creating a panel moulding: creating the running mould and then using the running mould to shape the plaster.

Creating a running mould

Different types of running moulds can be created for different types of product.

A simple design of running mould is for running straight or circular mouldings. The running mould will have two elements: a template of the shape to be formed and a frame to hold the template.

A template

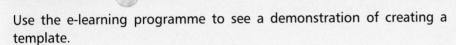

The template is created in zinc. Draw the profile of the moulding onto a piece of paper and then glue this to the zinc. Cut carefully through the zinc around the profile using a pair of snips, filing down to the profile line. Lay it on the original drawing to check that it matches. Finish by filing off any burrs. Make sure you remove the file marks as these will show on the finished moulding.

Prepare your template

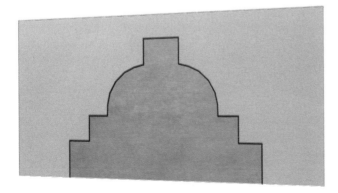

Mark out the shape

Cut out the shape and smooth edges

A frame to hold the template

Once you have created the template you will need to create a frame to fix it to. The frame will be pushed over the plaster to form the shape.

The frame consists of three parts:

- A stock to hold the zinc template.
- A horse or slipper fixed at right angles to the stock to support it.
- A brace fixed between the horse and the stock.

The stock should be cut 5mm behind the profile to allow for swelling. Splay the edge of the outline away from the template to prevent plaster clogging.

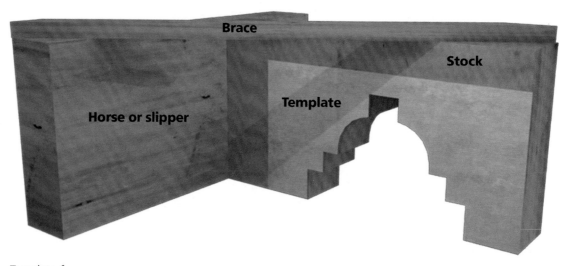

Template frame

Running out the moulding

Before starting, check the running area is clear and grease it to make sure the moulding can be easily removed afterwards.

1. Mix the plaster to a creamy consistency and pour a line of it along the running area.
2. Pull the running mould evenly across the plaster to begin to form the shape.
3. Add more mix and repeat two or three times to build up the mould. You should try to make as much of the mould in the first pass as possible.
4. Leave the moulding to set fully and then cut to size with a fine toothed saw and lots of water.
5. Clean the running mould immediately.

Prepare the work area

Run the mould

Leave to set

Fixing mouldings

E-LEARNING

Use the e-learning programme to see a demonstration of fixing mouldings.

The first thing to consider when fixing a cornice in place is to make sure you know which way round it goes. The wall line is the surface of the cornice which will fix to the wall and the ceiling line is the face which fixes to the ceiling.

The second part of the process is to cut the corners (known as mitres), of the cornice so that they butt up to each other.

1. Measure from the last fitted length of cornice to the corner and mark this measurement on the next length of cornice.

2. Place the length of cornice upside down in a **mitre** block.

3. Make sure that the ceiling line is at the base of the mitre block. If you are turning left on the wall, place the mitre block to the left of the cornice.

4. If the wall turns to the right, place the mitre block at the right of the cornice.

5. Support the cornice extending beyond the mitre block with a block of wood the same height as the mitre base to prevent the cornice breaking.

6. Cut the diagonal line depending upon whether it is an external or internal angle.

7. Fix the cornice to the wall either by drilling it in place or using adhesive.

Mitre Two 45° joints formed to make a right angle joint.

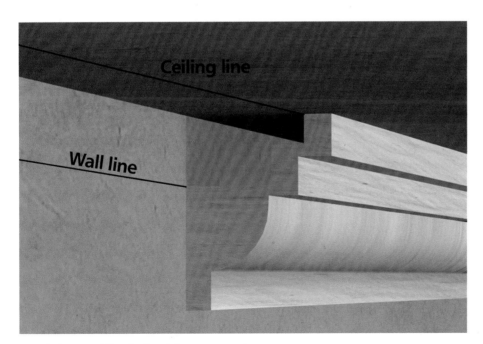

Check the moulding is the right way round

Cutting the mould for a left turn

Cutting the mould for a right turn

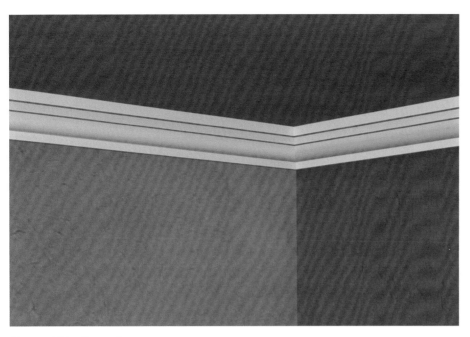

Fix mould to the wall

CHECKING FOR FAULTS

Once the work has been completed it will need to be checked for faults and against the original specification for the project.

Number and thickness of coats

The specification will have detailed the number of coats required. This will have been dependent upon the original background.

If there are insufficient coats then parts of the background may still be visible and the surface may be uneven. This could also be the case if the thickness of the coats is not specified. The thickness of the coats could also mean the material may not stick to the surface.

Finish

The finish will have been specified in the specification document and this will depend upon the final purpose of the surface. A wall that is to be painted needs to be finished to a higher smoothness than a wall at the back of a garage.

You will also need to check that there is no discolouration and that the finish is of an even appearance. Discolouration could be a result of too much iron in the sand.

Straight

The surface will also need to be checked to make sure it is straight, whether there are any cracks or hollows or bumps. This is something worth checking whilst you are working as these are easier to put right when the surface is still soft.

CHECK YOUR KNOWLEDGE

1. **On which surfaces would you typically use two coat work?**

   ☐ a. Plasterboard

   ☐ b. Brickwork

   ☐ c. Rough stone work

2. **If you a cutting a cornice that needs to turn left, where should you place the mitre block when cutting?**

   ☐ a. To the left of the cornice

   ☐ b. In the middle of the cornice

   ☐ c. To the right of the cornice

3. **What might cause a surface to discolour?**

   ☐ a. Too much salt in the sand

   ☐ b. Too much iron in the sand

   ☐ c. Too much clay in the sand

4. **When applying a skim coat to a wall, approximately how thick should it be?**

☐ a. 2 to 3mm

☐ b. 3 to 4mm

☐ c. 4 to 5mm

5. **True or False: The dot and screed method is also known as the plumb and dot method.**

☐ a. True

☐ b. False

Chapter 6

END TEST

END TEST OBJECTIVES

The end test will check your knowledge on the information held within this workbook.

The Test

1. **Solid plastering is the process of fitting sheets of plasterboard to a solid wall.**

   ☐ a. True

   ☐ b. False

2. **When does the plasterer generally arrive on site?**

   ☐ a. At the beginning of the project

   ☐ b. After the second fix work

   ☐ c. Before the first fix work

   ☐ d. After the first fix work

3. **Which type of trowel is shown?**

   ☐ a. Bucket trowel

   ☐ b. Angle trowel

   ☐ c. Gauging trowel

   ☐ d. Floating trowel

4. **A hawk is used to hold small quantities of material before applying it to the surface.**

   ☐ a. True

   ☐ b. False

5. **Which of these surfaces has a high absorbency?**

   ☐ a. Tiles

   ☐ b. Brickwork

   ☐ c. Aerated blocks

6. **After applying an undercoat to a surface, what tool can be used to create a key?**

   ☐ a. Float

   ☐ b. Devil float

   ☐ c. Hawk

   ☐ d. Gauging trowel

   ☐ e. Padsaw

   ☐ f. Brush

7. What are the absorbency rates of these background surfaces?

Write High, Low or Medium next to each surface.

Surface	Absorbency rate
Medium density blocks	
Aircrete blocks	
Dense blocks	
Common bricks	
Pre-cast concrete	
Glazed and painted	
Plasterboard	

8. What are the required steps to prepare the surface of an older building before rendering?

☐ a. Remove old render

☐ b. Rake out loose mortar joints

☐ c. Create a mechanical key

☐ d. Brush down surface

☐ e. Apply a chemical key

☐ f. Protect door and window openings

9. Which of the following qualities would you look for in a plasterer's sand used for rendering?

☐ a. The particles should be a range of sizes over 5mm

☐ b. The particles should be a range of sizes under 5mm

☐ c. It should contain no clay

☐ d. It should not be sourced from the sea

10. The tasks shown are required when preparing a plaster mix in a bucket. Number the tasks in the correct order.

Task	Step
Mix until even consistency	
Mix in all directions	
Add clean water	
Test with trowel	
Add remaining materials	
Add 50 per cent of plaster material	

11. How should bags of plaster be stored?

You can select more than one answer.

☐ a. In dry conditions

☐ b. In the back of the van

☐ c. Off the ground

☐ d. On the floor

12. Approximately, what size gap should you leave between plasterboard and the floor?

☐ a. 0mm

☐ b. 5mm

☐ c. 10mm

☐ d. 15mm

☐ e. 20mm

☐ f. 25mm

13. When storing plasterboard, it needs to be kept horizontally.

☐ a. True

☐ b. False

14. Name the different layers of the external render shown.

15. At which angles should a Tyrolean finish be applied?

You can select more than one answer.

☐ a. 15 degrees

☐ b. 30 degrees

☐ c. 45 degrees

☐ d. 60 degrees

☐ e. 75 degrees

☐ f. 90 degrees

16. You would typically use tapered edge plasterboards when dry lining.

☐ a. True

☐ b. False

17. In what order are the three coats applied? Number the coats in the correct order.

Task	Step
Skimming coat	
Render coat	
Floating coat	

18. What are the parts of a running mould?

19. What is the name of the method for applying a floating coat to achieve an absolutely plumb surface?

☐ a. Dot and screed

☐ b. Box screed

☐ c. Skimming coat

20. Approximately, how long is the curing process for a sand and cement floor screed?

☐ a. 7 hours

☐ b. 7 days

☐ c. 7 weeks

Answers to Check Your Knowledge and End Test

CHAPTER 1

1.

Task	Tool	Name
Keying the surface		Devil float
Wetting the surface		Brush
Measuring and mixing quantities of material		Bucket
Mixing small amounts of plaster and placing in awkward areas		Gauging trowel
Holding plaster prior to applying to surface		Hawk

2. **The gauging, bucket and plasterer's trowel**

3. **False: Fibrous plastering is used when making ornamental plasterwork such as cornices**

4. **False: Plasterers arrive on site after the first fix work**

5. **A: The gauging trowel**

CHAPTER 2

1. **A, D, F: When preparing an internal wall for plastering it you should test its absorbency, brush down to remove loose materials and apply a bonding agent if necessary**

2. **True: Suction is the ability of a background to absorb water**

3. **B: Plasterboard has a medium absorbency surface**

4. **False: A mechanical key is created using a range of tools to make a smooth surface rough**

CHAPTER 3

1. **C: The maximum size for a particle of plasterer's sand is 5mm**

2. **A,D: The two types of cement are hydraulic and non-hydraulic**

3.

Purpose	Type of plasterboard
Fire resistant plasterboard	
Standard plasterboard	
Moisture resistant plasterboard	
Acoustic performance plasterboard	

4. **True: Aggregate can include recycled concrete**

5. **B,C: The two types of lime are hydraulic and hydrated**

CHAPTER 4

1. **You will need 75kg of sand for each 25kg bag of cement for a ratio of 3:1**

2. **False: The scratch coat should be scored horizontally to allow curing water to be retained**

3. **True: Ashlar is a type of external render**

4. **C: The top coat would be the final coat**

CHAPTER 5

1. **B: Two coat work is typically used on brick or blockwork. You would only need to apply a single coat to plasterboard and rough stone work may require additional coat to fill in the hollows.**

2. **A: When cutting a cornice for a left turn, you should place it to the left in the mitre block**

3. **B: Too much iron in the sand could cause a rusty discolouration**

4. A: A skim coat should be approximately 2 to 3mm thick

5. True: Dot and screed can also be know as plumb and dot

CHAPTER 6

Please check your answers against the following. If any of the questions you answered are incorrect you are advised to go back to that section in the workbook or the e-learning programme to re-study.

Question 1

False: Plasterboard fitting is called drylining

Question 2

D: The plasterer usually arrives after the first fix and before the second fix

Question 3

A: The trowel shown is a bucket trowel

Question 4

True: You place material on your hawk and use in conjunction with your trowel to apply material to the surface

Question 5

C: The aerated blocks will have the highest absorbency

Question 6

B: Devil float

Question 7

Surface	Absorbency rate
Medium density blocks	Medium
Aircrete blocks	High
Dense blocks	Low
Common bricks	Medium
Pre-cast concrete	Low
Glazed and painted	Low
Plasterboard	Medium

Question 8

A, B, D, F: You should always remove the old render, remove any loose mortar joints, brush down the surface and protect any openings. Other steps may be required in certain circumstances.

Question 9

B, D: The particles should be a range of sizes (and under 5mm) and it should contain some clay to aid spreadability. Sand sourced from the sea will contain too much salt so should be avoided.

Question 10

Task	Step
Mix until even consistency	5
Mix in all directions	3
Add clean water	1
Test with trowel	6
Add remaining materials	4
Add 50 per cent of plaster material	2

Question 11

A, C: Bags of plaster should be stored off the ground in dry conditions

Question 12

D: 15mm

Question 13

A: Plasterboard should be stored horizontally to protect it from damage

Question 14

Background, dubbing out coat, scratch coat, top coat

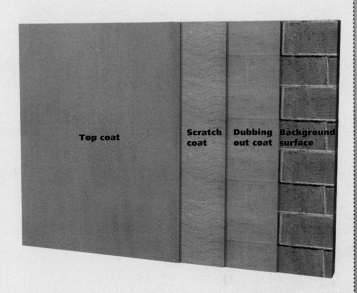

Top coat | Scratch coat | Dubbing out coat | Background surface

Question 15

C, F: A Tyrolean finish should be applied at angles of 45 degrees from the left, 45 degrees from the right then at 90 degrees straight on

Question 16

A: A tapered edge plasterboard would typically be used if you were dry lining

Question 17

Task	Step
Skimming coat	3
Render coat	1
Floating coat	2

Question 18

Stock, brace, horse or slipper, template

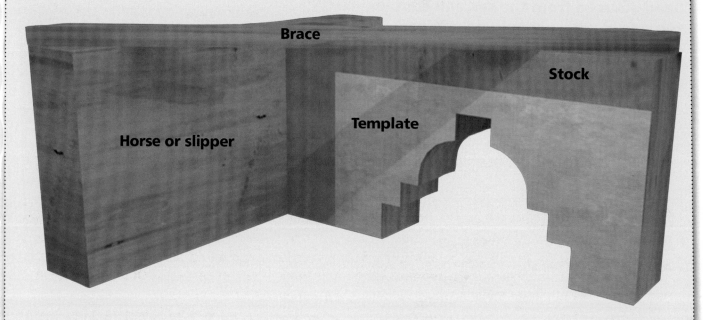

Brace

Stock

Horse or slipper

Template

Question 19

A: Dot and screed

Question 20

B: The curing time for a sand and cement floor screed is approximately 7 days

Glossary

Additives A range of substances that can be added to mixtures to improve the strength of the mix or to control the timing in achieving the desired mix

Adhesive General term given for a range of bonding agents

Aggregate The name given to the range of particulates used in construction. These can include sand, gravel and crushed stone

Angle bead Steel strips fixed at external corners to provide a continuous guide when plastering

Ashlar An external finish with marked lines on the plainface render to imitate stone work

Background General term used for the surface to which materials are adhered

Block The most common block type is aggregate concrete blocks. They have a large number of desirable properties including high sound and thermal insulation and excellent moisture, fire and frost resistance. They are strong, lightweight, easy to work with and easy to fix to. Blocks are manufactured in solid, hollow and cellular block forms and one type of block can be used in every situation on a site

Blockwork Walls built of blocks as opposed to bricks; may be used externally, with a rendered finish, but more widely for the internal walls of a cavity wall

Brickwork A solid wall built of bricks, laid to bond and in mortar. Used to be the most common load-bearing external wall construction. Mainly finished with fair faced bricks and pointed or rendered. Minimal maintenance required but as properties age partial or complete re-pointing or re-rendering respectively may become necessary

Bucket trowel A trowel with a square metal edge used for scraping material from the bottom of the bucket

Building line One of the lines set by the local building authority; the building must not be constructed in front of this line

Cavity The gap between the internal and external walls of a building. Usually 50mm wide to increase the thermal insulation and weather resistance of the wall. The cavity must be kept clear and not bridged (except for wall ties and insulation). A damp proof course (DPC) must be provided around the perimeter of openings in cavity walls otherwise dampness can occur internally

Cement A grey or white powdery material made from chalk or limestone and clay. Cement is the most common binder in bricklaying mortar and works by hardening as a result of a chemical reaction when mixed with water. The most common type of cement is Ordinary Portland Cement (OPC)

Chemical key A method of creating a key to the background to ensure materials applied to the background stick. Achieved by applying bonding agent (e.g. PVA)

Cornice A decorative moulding at the junction between the walls and ceiling of a room

Course A row of bricks, concrete blocks, etc. in a wall

Coving A curved moulding at the junction between the walls and ceiling of a room – a form of cornice

Curing The method of preventing the loss of water in concrete foundations by slowing the chemical reaction of hydration as the strength of the concrete cannot be maximized if it is dried too quickly. Curing usually takes up to seven days and there are a number of ways concrete can be cured including covering with damp hessian or polythene sheets, or spraying the concrete with a curing compound. However during colder times, the hessian should be dry to prevent frosting

Damp proof course (DPC) A horizontal layer of impervious materials such as bituminous felt, asphalt, two courses of slate or two courses of engineering bricks. It is usually laid at 150mm above ground level to prevent moisture rising. For walls subject to high compressive loads. It is also necessary to form an impervious barrier in cavity walls when bridging openings (e.g. doors and windows). Damp proof course is commonly known as DPC

Darby rule A straight-edged rule used to level off surfaces

Devil float A float with nails protruding from the bottom used to scratch backgrounds for plastering or rendering to ensure materials stick to the background

EML The standard and widely used abbreviation for expanded metal lathing

Engineering brick A strong and dense type of brick, impervious to water so ideal for use in damp areas

Ethylene vinyl acetate (EVA) A type of bonding agent commonly known as EVA

EVA The standard and widely used abbreviation for ethylene vinyl acetate

Expanded metal lathing (EML) A diamond shaped meshed steel used to cover irregular surfaces or surfaces where two different materials meet and will be plastered over. It can be made from galvanized or stainless steel for use internally or externally

Feather edge A straight-edged rule used to level off surfaces

Fibrous plasterwork Decorative plasterwork that is usually made off-site

Finishing coat The final top coat in plastering also known as setting coat or skimming coat

Floats A range of tools which can be made from a variety of materials with a grip that holds a thin flat base approximately 100mm × 250mm. There are a number of different floats for

different purposes including plasterer's float, devil float and grout float

Floating coat A backing coat which provides a surface for the final coat known as the finishing, setting or skimming coat

Floor screed The final layer of concrete laid on top of the oversite concrete to level off. The floor screed is usually laid later on in the project

Footlifter A metal tool used for holding a tacked down plasterboard in place whilst it's being fixed

Gauging trowel A popular trowel used for the mixing, bedding and placing of materials

Glaze A ceramic coating in a glassy state or the material from which this coating is made

Gypsum A type of mineral mined and quarried across the world. Usually sourced in the country where it will be used due to its low value and bulky properties. Gypsum can also be created as a by-product from other industrial processes

Hacking A method of creating a key to the background to ensure materials applied to the background stick. Achieved by physically hacking a background with a scutch hammer

Hawk A square metal piece with a handle for holding small quantities of materials (e.g. plaster) for easy reach when applying to wall

Hessian A coarse fabric used to cover the concrete foundations during the curing process

Jointing The process of finishing off mortar joints in brickwork or blockwork to waterproof the wall. Timing is crucial for jointing as the mortar may crumble if jointing is carried out after the mortar has dried

Joist A beam that supports a ceiling or floor

Key The preparation to backgrounds either chemically, mechanically, hacking or scratching before plaster or render is applied. Creating keys ensures that the plaster or render sticks and the method of keying will depend on the type of background

Laser level A mechanical device mounted on a stand which extends to the height of the room. The laser level projects the horizontal and vertical levels onto the surface using laser beams

Level The horizontal level of a surface or structure

Levelling The process of using a spirit level to check and mark levels

Lime There are two types of lime, hydraulic and non-hydraulic. They can both be used for mortar and pointing. The difference is in the setting time. The ratio for a lime mortar mix is six parts sand, one part lime and one part cement. Production and sustainability benefits make lime an eco-friendly material

Mechanical key The recess in mortar joints by 10mm between brickwork or blockwork before plastering or rendering to ensure the plaster or render sticks

Mitre Two 45° joints formed to make a right angle joint

Mortar A mixture of sand, cement (sometimes with lime and/or additives) and water, used to bond stones and bricks. Can be mixed by hand or mechanically on or off site

Noggings Short horizontal timber struts fitted between studs in a timber stud wall

OPC The standard and widely used abbreviation for ordinary Portland cement (see below)

Ordinary Portland cement (OPC) One of the raw ingredients of mortar, made from crushed limestone or clay mixed with water which is then heated at very high temperatures and ground into a powder form

Pebble dashing An external render finish where pebbles or similar aggregate materials are thrown onto a fresh coat of render. Two coats are applied consisting of a scratch coat and a second or butter coat

Perimeter The total length of the boundary to a closed shape, e.g. a room inside a building

Personal protective equipment (PPE) Depending on the type of work, there are different types of equipment specifically designed to protect your health and safety. Examples include gloves, safety boots, goggles and dust mask

Plainface render An external render finish commonly used which generally consists of three coats: the spatterdash coat, scratch coat and floating coat

Plaster A colourless, white or pinkish mineral formed from heating gypsum at high temperatures. Plaster is used to protect and enhance the appearance of the surface as it provides a joint-less finish

Plasterboard A type of board made of gypsum sandwiched between sheets of paper. It has a number of properties and can be made to different thicknesses and sizes for different areas and uses

Plasticizer An additive that increases fluidity or plasticity of a mortar, cement paste or concrete mixture and reduces water content and drying times. Plasticizers improve the workability of a mortar mix but should not be used in structural work without the permission of the structural engineer

Plasterer's float A float used for render work

Plasterer's trowel A trowel when new is used for applying plaster undercoats, but when used and worn with slightly rounded edges it is used for finishing plaster coats

Plumb The vertical level of a surface or structure

Plumb bob A weight attached to the plumb line, for checking vertical lines and providing a guide for constructing gable end walls

Polyvinyl acetate (PVA) A type of bonding agent commonly known as PVA

PPE The standard and widely used abbreviation for personal protective equipment

PVA The standard and widely used abbreviation for polyvinyl acetate

RCD The standard and widely used abbreviation for residual current device

Render A sand and cement backing coat for tiling, usually applied in at least two coats

Rendering The application of render to external wall surfaces for appearance or to make the wall waterproof. Cracks may appear and should be repaired as progressively this will weather and lose key allowing water to get behind render. This causes saturation of the wall which can result in fungal decay of structural timbers internally

Residual current device A safety cut-out device to protect you from electric shock recommended for use when using cement mixers

Retarder An additive used to extend the setting time of a mortar mix

Rough cast An external render similar to pebble dashing but the pebbles or other aggregate are mixed in with the second or butter coat

Sand Fine aggregate that is one of the raw ingredients for mixing mortar

SBR The standard and widely used abbreviation for styrene butadiene rubber

Scratch coat The first coat applied to the wall when three coat work is required, keyed with a devil float

Screed A narrow band of material used as a guide when applying plaster undercoats

Setting coat The final top coat in plastering also known as finishing coat or skimming coat

Scutch hammer A doubled-end hammer with long thin steel blades about 30mm wide acting as chisels. The scutch hammer is used for hacking the surfaces of brickwork to create a key for rendering

Skimming coat The final top coat in plastering also known as finishing coat or setting coat

Spirit level A tool used to check true vertical and horizontal lines indicated by a bubble in spirit-filled vials

Spot board A piece of ply placed on a stand that is used as a holding area for larger amounts of material (e.g. plaster). The plasterer will generally transfer the materials from the spot board to the hawk ready for applying to the surface

Stud The timber posts within a timber-frame wall

Stud wall An internal, non-load-bearing timber-frame wall faced with lath and plaster or plasterboard

Styrene butadiene rubber A water resistant bonding agent that can be used to improve the properties of sand/cement renders, floor screeds and mortars

Trowels A range of hand held tools used to mix, apply, spread or remove materials. There are many different types of trowels for different purposes including bucket trowel, gauge trowel, notched trowel and pointing trowel

Tyrolean finish An external render finish formed by spraying materials onto the surface using a Tyrolean gun to create a textured finish

Index